Mer
The High IQ Society

The Complete Book of

Personality
Tests

THIS IS A CARLTON BOOK

Published by Carlton Books Limited
an imprint of the Carlton Publishing Group
20 Mortimer Street
London W1T 3JW

10 9 8 7 6 5 4 3 2

A catalogue record for this book is available from the British Library

ISBN 978-1-84732-427-6

Printed in Great Britain by CPI MacKays, Chatham, ME5 8TD

The content of this book was previously published in
Assess Your Personality and *The Book of Total Genius*

Mensa
The High IQ Society

The Complete Book of

Personality Tests

Learn about and develop
your personality quotient!

BREMNER • CARTER • FULTON • RUSSELL

CARLTON
BOOKS

WHAT IS MENSA?

Mensa is the international society for people with a high IQ.
We have more than 100,000 members in over 40 countries worldwide.

The society's aims are:
    to identify and foster human intelligence for the benefit of humanity
    to encourage research in the nature, characteristics, and uses of intelligence
    to provide a stimulating intellectual and social environment for its members

Anyone with an IQ score in the top two per cent of the population is eligible to
become a member of Mensa – are you the 'one in 50' we've been looking for?

Mensa membership offers an excellent range of benefits:
    Networking and social activities nationally and around the world
    Special Interest Groups – hundreds of chances to pursue your hobbies
        and interests – from art to zoology!
    Monthly members' magazine and regional newsletters
    Local meetings – from games challenges to food and drink
    National and international weekend gatherings and conferences
    Intellectually stimulating lectures and seminars
    Access to the worldwide SIGHT network for travellers and hosts

For more information about Mensa: www.mensa.org, or

British Mensa Ltd.,
St John's House,
St John's Square,
Wolverhampton
WV2 4AH
Telephone: +44 (0) 1902 772771
E-mail: enquiries@mensa.org.uk
www.mensa.org.uk

CONTENTS

Introduction

This is, I have to tell you, not a very respectable book. The reason? It does something that you are never supposed to do, and that is to combine psychometrics with popular psychology. Yet I make no apology for treating the subject in what to psychologists may appear a rather flippant manner. In the first place my information about psychometric personality assessment is accurate and is not in any way mixed with information about less 'respectable' methods. If you are easily offended by anything that is not 'real' psychology then please regard the book as two separate volumes within one cover. The first part contains information, told in what I hope is an accessible, anecdotal and interesting yet accurate manner, about psychometric personality testing. This is important because psychometric testing is rapidly becoming an everyday tool for personnel selection and development. Or, put more brutally, if you want a job or promotion, you're probably going to get tested. It therefore makes sense to understand what testing is, what it does, what it cannot do, and how tests are constructed and administered.

The second half of the book is fun and games. I make no other claims for it, and if you feel that fun and science should not be found within the same covers, then you have every right to that opinion, but that is not the stance that I will take. My point is that, on an everyday level, personality assessment goes on all the time. It is an important part of human psychology, and in a purely intuitive way we all do it on a daily basis. Every time we see someone unfamiliar, every time we meet a new acquaintance, every time a new colleague is taken on at the office, everyone concerned forms opinions of that person's personality. Sometimes these opinions will be used for nothing more than fueling the office gossip machine, but on other occasions they may well be used to make quite important decisions about the person concerned. Take, for example, the police. Do they ask a suspect to complete a psychometric personality test as part of their interrogation? On rare occasions they may, but in the vast majority of cases they rely on gut feeling, hunches, intuition, whatever you want to call it. And the subject of their investigations may go to jail purely on the strength of such hunches. So, though popular personality assessment may be subject to severe disapprobation from the psychological establishment, and even though that disapprobation may be fully justified, it is a fact of life, a thing that people have built into their mental make-up. It does affect the way we live, and therefore I would submit that its place in this book is justified. However, I will at all times keep what I regard as 'popular, intuitive' methods separate from mainstream psychology. Even then I shall be in trouble, for many adherents of graphology, body language, color analysis, etc., regard their methods as at least as successful, if not more so, as those used by psychometricians. You will have the chance to judge for yourself.

Personality assessment, though not necessarily known by that name, is as old as humanity. Because people live in society and because they are bound together by the bonds of competition and cooperation, it has always been important for us to understand each other's personalities. One may well imagine that when our hunter-gatherer ancestors finally cornered a beast they had been pursuing, it would have been of the greatest importance to know which hunter would remain brave when the animal tried to break out, and which would flee. Similarly, the competitive side of human nature requires people to size each other up, look for weaknesses in a rival, and search for the opportunity to come out on top. Courtiers and politicians would have sized each other up trying to decide who, out of a tricky bunch of customers, was the most tricky and who, for the moment at least, might make a useful ally. The number of situations where humans need to understand each other's motives, instincts and likely reactions is almost limitless.

Beyond any real need for information, humans seem to be just plain curious about each other. If you are the type who finds other people interesting, you will doubtless have spent many hours chatting to your friends about the motives, quirks and relationships of other friends or, for that matter, enemies. You will not be surprised to hear that you are far from unique. Most of us do it, and where, for example, would gossip be without a hefty dose of personality assessment? But there is more to it than mere amusement. As communal creatures, the success of our society – indeed, its very survival – is dependent on our constantly assessing and re-assessing each other. Situations change, as do people to a greater or lesser extent, and the results of those changes have effects, trivial or profound, on our communities and societies. It is largely by instinct that we keep ourselves up to date on these matters. In addition to understanding the personalities of others we also have a great need to understand ourselves, and this, to the surprise of many, is an area that people often find extremely difficult. Life presents us with a series of choices that stretches from the cradle (teddy bear or fuzzy rabbit?) to the grave (buried or cremated?) Our whole lives are governed by the choices we make, and those choices will be affected fundamentally by our personality. In employment it will be important to know whether we prefer to work with other people or alone, whether we value money more than status or job satisfaction, whether we like to be outdoors or in an office. Away from work we have to decide who to marry – or, of course, whether to marry – whether to have children, and if so, how many. The list just goes on and on. The rather strange thing is that so many people are very bad at knowing what their own personality is really like. I spend a great deal of time working with people who are experiencing problems at work or in relationships that are, at root, caused by a fundamental ignorance of their own personality. Even stranger is the fact that once you have pointed out to these people what your assessment has discovered, they say, 'Oh yes, that's exactly what I'm like!'

There is much more to self-assessment than purely utilitarian matters. We are actively interested in what we are like. Huge amounts of time are spent in self-analysis of one sort or another. In modern times, and especially since the advent of psychoanalysis, this search for self-knowledge has become almost a plague, and hardly a day passes without some new fad or theory that adds to the already bewildering array. To some extent this may be symptomatic of societies where people are so affluent and have so little concern about how to keep themselves fed and housed that they have enormous leisure for introspection. But that is only a development of an urge that has been with us for thousands of years. Great writers, philosophers, doctors and religious leaders in every country and from every era have ventured theories concerning what motivates people. And such theories have been received with great enthusiasm because deep in our hearts we all think that we are extremely interesting beings and well worth close examination.

Since I have mentioned the early history of personality assessment, we should take a quick look at the history of this art. Let's start with an ancient Greek philosopher called Theophrastus. He wrote a series of sketches entitled *The Characters* in which he included well-known stereotypes such as the Flatterer, the Coward, and so on. His descriptions of these types are completely familiar to us today, and we could all think of people who would fit them. Greek playwrights also dealt with well-known personality types. Greek actors wore masks called *persona* and it is these that give us the word 'personality.' When the audience saw an actor in his mask they knew immediately what to expect of his character. This idea of treating people as types has continued throughout history and surfaces centuries later in the *commedia dell'arte* of the Italian Renaissance with its familiar character types, such as the handsome hero, the sly servant and the jealous husband. We can see it in Hollywood movies, even very modern ones, in which you may still find the 'Tart with a Heart,' for example, who would have been familiar to audiences hundreds of years earlier. Modern TV soap operas also use such characters, and the viewer knows straightaway who represents the nosy neighbor, the pretty young girl, or the villainous trickster.

Nor is this way of regarding personality peculiar to western culture. Japanese drama used masked characters whose features gave the audience an immediate insight into their personality, and traditional Chinese opera used a formal system of make-up that provided the audience with the same information (heroes had a lot of red in their make-up; evil characters had white).

The attempt to assess personality has persisted and has spawned a huge variety of methods – some quite bizarre, and some still having their adherents today. Phrenology, or reading the bumps of the head, was popular in the last century and was seriously considered to reveal inner truths about the subject's personality. Graphology, or the study of handwriting, was, and is, popular. Though widely dismissed by scientists, it is widely practised and given credence by many. In France especially, graphology still commands a considerable amount of respect in some quarters. It is easy to see why. Common sense tells us that something as intimately connected to a person as their handwriting does indeed reveal personality. We have all seen examples that seem 'typical' of a certain person's character. It is when you try to construct a system based on such findings that you discover there is no solid basis for believing that handwriting is indicative of character. In recent times other fads have arisen that claim to be able to indicate personality. Color analysis was one such which, for a while in the 1970s, was considered by some to have something useful to contribute. People were attracted to the idea that a person's choice of colors might be indicative of their personality type. Great theories were constructed in which red became the color of assertiveness, yellow was associated with intellect, and so on. We will take a closer look at some of the less orthodox methods of personality assessment later.

What of mainstream psychology? What does it have to offer by way of personality assessment? Let's go back for a moment to the types described by Theophrastus. There was an underlying assumption that these held constant over time. The Garrulous Man remained talkative in any company, whether his conversation was welcome or not. Similarly, the Coward could be relied upon to behave without courage, and the Fool would always be stupid. These types are distantly but quite clearly related to what modern psychologists call 'traits.' It is widely assumed these days that someone who, when tested, shows a marked tendency to be sociable and outgoing will be so regularly and will remain so over time. This will also apply to other traits such as anxiety or creativity. Most of the personality analysis carried out in business and commerce today relies upon 'trait theory' as its basis.

However, there are other theories of personality that we should mention. Those who favor a behavioral approach would say that personality is shaped by our reactions to external circumstances both now and in the past. Others would have us believe that all our actions stem from the promptings of unconscious urges that may be so deeply buried we are completely unaware of them. This is known technically as psychodynamic theory and stems largely from the work of Sigmund Freud. In recent years unconscious urges have been very popular as an explanation for behavior. This has led to some bizarre and even sinister developments. Some psychotherapists, especially in the US, have championed the idea that women who have been sexually abused in childhood bury these traumatic events so deeply in their unconscious that memories of what occurred can only be restored by a period of intense therapy. Women who thought they had had a happy, or at least unexceptional, childhood have been urged to recover the most painful memories of abuse. This has been, unsurprisingly, a very controversial issue. The problem about unconscious urges is that they are unconscious. Who is to arbitrate as to whether they are present and to what extent they are responsible for a person's behavior? Naturally, some psychologists and psychiatrists are anxious to lay claim to this area of expertise. Others are not so sure.

As trait theory is the predominant method in use today, let's examine in some detail how it works. Our old friends the Greeks, not content with classifying dramatic characters, also came up with four main 'types' into which people could be sorted. In about 400BC Hippocrates concluded that people could be sanguine (blood: optimistic, hopeful), phlegmatic (phlegm: apathetic), choleric (bile: irascible), or melancholic (black bile: sad, depressed). So successful were these classifications that they were further developed by Galen in the second century AD and are still familiar to us today. However, the system was too clumsy. People do not fit neatly into one category or another.

That did not prevent later scientists from trying another classification by type, but this time the deciding factor was body shape. This theory was well explained for the layman by the psychologist Eric Berne:

A human being comes from an egg. As that egg develops, it forms a three-layered tube and the three layers develop into different body organs. The inner layer becomes the stomach and lungs, the middle layer into bones, joints, muscles, and blood vessels, and the outer layer into the skin and nervous system. As the embryo develops, these three systems grow about equally and, when the baby is finally born, it will have roughly equal amounts of gut, muscle and brain. However, differences do occur and we can easily observe that some people have a much larger amount of gut, some are noticeably broad and muscular, and others have a more developed brain.

The theory of body types divides these people up according to their physique and gives them names accordingly. The people who are round and fat because they have a more developed gut are called endomorphs, the broad, muscular ones are known as mesomorphs, and the thin, long, ones are known as ectomorphs.

Now comes the tricky bit. According to some writers these types also appear to describe certain people very well, and the fat, jolly man or the broad, muscular, hearty sportsman are types with which we are all familiar. There is also a general feeling that clever people should be skinny, tall and have larger heads. Psychologists, who are very good at making up names for things (even when they are not quite sure that they exist), have invented names for personality types based on body shape. Thus the person whose physique is dominated by the gut is a viscerotonic endomorph. This is what Berne says about this type:

His abdomen is big because he has lots of intestines. He likes to take things in. He likes to take in food, and affection and approval as well. Going to a banquet with people who like him is his idea of a fine time.

The next type is the somatotonic mesomorph. Berne says:

He would rather breathe than eat. He has a bony head, big shoulders, and a square jaw . . . Li'l Abner and other men of action belong to this type. Such men make good lifeguards and construction workers.

The cerebrotonic ectomorph, on the other hand, has a long body shape and thin bones and muscles. 'He looks like an absent-minded professor and often is one,' according to Berne. Such a person is likely to be nervous, jumpy, and not very keen on action. They are much better suited to reflective pursuits than anything else.

Having established this as a theory, can we use it to make predictions about people's behavior? The first and most obvious objection is simply that most people do not fit neatly into any of these categories. I know in my own case that I rather enjoy eating (and my figure suffers for it), I work with my brain rather than my body, but I also walk, run, cycle and work out at the gym. I'm sure that I am not unique; most of the people you see in any street would be hard to place firmly as any of the three types we have discussed.

Does this theory hold up at all? Does it actually tell us anything useful? Surely all it offers is some fairly obvious statements such as, for example, big, muscular hearty people are big, muscular and hearty. Even if that is true, it is hardly illuminating. Personality assessment, to be of any value, must be able to predict with some accuracy what a person will do in a variety of situations. The body type theory does not do that. For example, will the viscerotonic endomorph be aesthetically sensitive? Tense? Socially bold? Self-doubting? The theory is just too simplistic to answer any of these questions. It is interesting as a curiosity, but for serious purposes it has no use.

The next major milestone in personality theory was laid by Carl Gustav Jung. He had been a follower and close colleague of Freud's. Although they eventually fell out over theoretical differences, he advocated a theory that was much influenced by Freudian concepts. Jung talked of a psyche, which was made up of the ego and the unconscious, which itself took two forms: personal and collective. These systems were separate but interacted with each other. The personal unconscious consists of repressed individual experiences and is a concept quite familiar to us today. The collective unconscious also still has its proponents but is much more controversial. Jung held that the whole of humanity has access to a common unconscious and that this explains why all people react in a broadly similar way.

It was Jung who divided humanity into extroverts and introverts. Extroverts have an orientation toward the external, real world, while introverts prefer to look inward to their subjective experiences. People do not necessarily fall neatly into one category or the other, and even the most introverted among us have times when they are focused outwards. However, in the conscious mind one of these orientations will predominate. These basic orientations operate in conjunction with four functions that exist in all individuals. It is the interaction of orientation and function that forms the basis of personality. The four functions are:

- **Sensing:** the reality function which gives factual representations of the world.

- **Intuition:** an unconscious process that looks beyond the surface of the 'real' world in the search for underlying factors that help an individual to comprehend the essence of reality.

- **Thinking:** the rational observation of the world in terms of fact, logic and argument.

- **Feeling:** an evaluative observation of self and the world in terms of emotions.

Sensing versus intuition, and thinking versus feeling are known as the two functions. One of the preferred functions is the dominant function and the other is the auxiliary. Thus an individual who is more sensing than intuiting and more thinking than feeling might have sensing as his dominant function and thinking as his auxiliary type. For another person who is also a sensing and thinking type, thinking might be the dominant function and sensing the auxiliary. The dominant function is used in the preferred attitude (extroversion or introversion). Introverts use their dominant function in the inner world; extroverts use their dominant function in the outer world. Conversely, the auxiliary function is used in the non-preferred attitude.

To determine a person's dominant and auxiliary function, psychologists Myers and Briggs derived an additional scale, judgement versus perception, in which a four-letter code can be used to indicate the individual's type. The judgement/perception (J-P) preference indicates the function that an individual uses when dealing with the outer world. Thus if judgement is preferred, either feeling or thinking (whichever is preferred) is used most in the outer world. If perception is preferred, either sensing or intuition (whichever is preferred) is used most in the outside world. The dominant function varies for extroverts and introverts. For extroverts the function to which J-P points is the dominant function and the other is the auxiliary. For introverts the reverse is the case. This Jungian typology, despite its age, is still very widely used in personality analysis.

Long after Jung, another psychologist, Hans Eysenck, produced a different typology, which has also received much attention (summarized in the diagram overleaf).

Eysenck's work is a good illustration of trait theory in action. A trait is simply a description of a habitual behavior pattern. Our language contains literally thousands of words that describe such patterns. These range from 'sociability' and 'persistence' to 'anxiety' and 'instability.' Many psychologists have tried to construct questionnaires to identify which of these traits describes a particular respondent. These seek to elicit information about the respondent's preferences, opinions and attitudes, the most common type being one that makes a series of statements with which the respondent is invited to agree or disagree. As there may be occasions on which no hard-and-fast answer can be given, there is usually a third option for those who wish to remain 'undecided.' In some tests the responses are more finely graded and will allow the respondent to answer on a five-point scale that goes from 1 (strongly agree) to 5 (strongly disagree), with 3 representing the point at which no firm

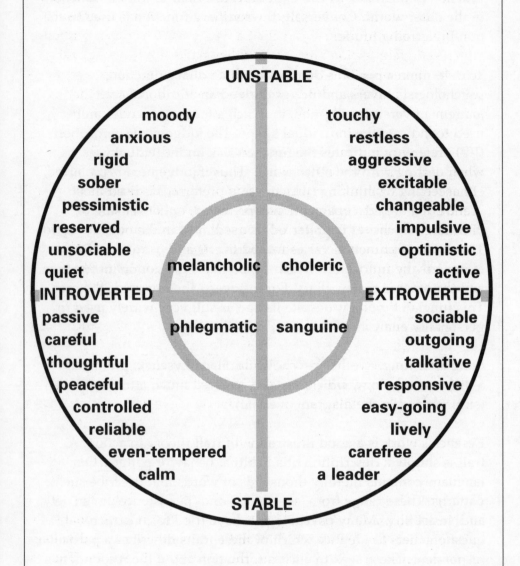

UNSTABLE

moody   touchy
anxious   restless
rigid   aggressive
sober   excitable
pessimistic   changeable
reserved   impulsive
unsociable   optimistic
quiet   **melancholic choleric** active

INTROVERTED   **EXTROVERTED**

passive   sociable
careful **phlegmatic sanguine** outgoing
thoughtful   talkative
peaceful   responsive
controlled   easy-going
reliable   lively
even-tempered   carefree
calm   a leader

STABLE

Eysenck's Typology

decision can be made. The important feature of such questionnaires is that they do not have right or wrong answers. A statement such as 'I like going to parties' can elicit a 'yes' or 'no' response without the respondent feeling anxious that they have 'got it wrong.' Of course, there are circumstances in which respondents try to create an artificial impression of themselves but we will come to that later.

The history of psychometric personality assessment began during the First World War when the American army was keen to ascertain whether recruits were emotionally disturbed before sending them into action. A questionnaire was devised, and investigated issues such as 'Do you wet the bed?' and 'Do you daydream frequently?' If it seemed that the respondent exhibited too many symptoms of this sort, he would be sent for further examination.

At first it seemed that the main use of such techniques would be medical. A famous test from the early days of personality assessment was the Minnesota Multiphasic Personality Inventory which sought to identify disorders such as depression, paranoia, schizophrenia, and psychopathic deviance. However, it eventually became clear that the real commercial value of such tests lay in their ability to help employers with staff selection and development. This is the area with which the first part of this book is mainly concerned.

There are so many personality tests available that it is reasonable to ask whether they are all equally valid and whether, if an individual is tested on several different tests, the results will be similar. The short answer is 'no.' It is true that those tests that rely on trait theory and that look at similar traits should produce broadly similar results. However, some tests are completely different. For example, the well-known Rorschach Inkblot Test is an example of a so-called projective technique in which the subject is asked to 'see' things in a series of colored blobs. The interpretation of the results of such tests is highly subjective and depends very largely on the skill of the psychologist involved.

It is also worth noting right at the start that not everything that looks like a psychometric test actually is one. The plethora of tests that appear in magazines and newspapers are strictly for fun and have no real psychological value. Rather more sinister are tests that purport to be psychometric but that rely heavily on the so-called 'Barnum effect' for their results. P.T. Barnum, you will recall, was the showman who coined the phrase, 'There's a sucker born every minute.' It is quite easy to come up with a test that will provide a report that is applicable to everyone and does not differentiate between individuals at all. It is also easy to ensure that all the people who receive a report from such a test will believe it to be an accurate picture of themselves.

Can you change?

The question of whether personality can be changed is vital to the whole area of personality assessment. Unfortunately, as with many questions in psychology, the answer is not straightforward. Part of the very definition of personality is (as we saw earlier) that it should be stable over time. You get up each morning the same person that went to bed last night. This is certainly our common experience of ourselves and the people we know, and we would be wary of someone who was subject to such violent personality changes that they seemed to become a different person within a short space of time. There are, indeed, examples of people with multiple personality disorder who do switch from one personality to another totally different one within a very short space of time. But we regard this as a psychiatric condition requiring medical intervention and not as in any way the norm. However, if people cannot change, then the benefits of personality assessment are much reduced. We can pick out people who might be suitable or unsuitable for particular situations. We can look at people working together and see who is likely to get on well and who is not. But if we cannot help people to change, then our role is a limited one.

The extent to which people are in control of their personality is controversial. Freud and Jung would have us believe that we are largely subject to the promptings of unconscious urges. This view has affected many areas of thought over the last century. In the arts, for example, it has been almost compulsory among academics to hold to the view that the artist is the last person to understand the work he or she has created. A novel, for example, is said to be full of the unconscious promptings of the author's psyche, and the author is ill-equipped to understand these promptings by virtue of the fact that, as they are unconscious, he or she is unaware of them.

Psychoanalysis is based on the principle that people will go on repeating a vicious circle of neurotic behavior until a qualified psychoanalyst helps them unravel the motives that drive them.

This process is a very lengthy and expensive one and any change in behavior is only obtained after the most searching examination of the subject's childhood, formative experiences and relationships. A number of techniques, such as free association and dream analysis, are used in an attempt to get the patient to face the urges that have been hidden for so long. As much of the unconscious material consists of repressed memories of episodes in the patient's past that are too painful to be recalled, you may understand that the effort of uncovering such memories is considerable.

At the other extreme we find the existentialist school, which teaches that we need not be bound by our past, and urges us to take personal responsibility for our lives. The message could not be more different. This is a passage from *Theory and Practice of Counselling and Psychotherapy* by Gerald Corey:

> *The existential view of human nature is captured, in part, by the notion that the significance of our existence is never fixed once and for all; rather, we continually recreate ourselves through our projects. Humans are in a constant state of transition, emerging, evolving, and becoming. Being a person implies that we are discovering and making sense of existence. We pose questions such as 'Who am I? Who have I been? Who can I become? Where am I going?' There are no pre-existing designs and no meanings that are assigned or given to us.*

On a day-to-day basis we know that people do change. Usually the changes are small and happen over a long period, but they can be sudden and dramatic. Take, for example, someone who suffers the death of a partner. This may well result in a period of depression that could last months or even years, and in the long term we might notice a number of changes such as increased anxiety, a less extrovert orientation, even an increase in self-doubt and a decline in creativity. None of these changes would be set in stone, and if we were to imagine that our subject eventually meets a new partner, then we might see other more positive changes over time.

When we are testing people in an occupational setting we are continually aware of the possibility that changes in personality can be made. The particular report I use most has two sections at the end. The first is Potential Strengths, which, as you would expect, highlights positive areas that the subject should be encouraged to emphasize. The second section is Potential Development Needs, which, put plainly, is a list of things that are not an asset and that might benefit from change. One of the things we emphasize to clients is that your personality is not something fixed like, say, your shoe size, but something that, within certain limits, is capable of change. What those limits are is open to question. I should imagine that if an employee were to be called in for an appraisal interview after testing and was told, 'You could make management and get a pay rise if you could just learn to be a bit more friendly and outgoing with the customers,' the requirement might well be within that person's capability. Self-interest seems to be a powerful motivating factor in making such changes.

All changes in personality are likely to be stressful; therefore it makes sense to take things slowly. Start by working on aspects of your personality that you feel you could change without too much trouble. Remember that a dramatic change is unlikely to last.

What is almost certainly impossible and definitely ill-advised is the attempt to become a person you are quite clearly not. It is fairly common to come across the sort of self-help books that promise the gullible reader the chance to acquire a new, more forceful, more dynamic personality. Naturally, the come-on at some point suggests that this 'new you' will also be more attractive to the opposite sex. Oh dear. The chance of such a bold enterprise ever succeeding must be almost incalculably small. It is not possible that a painfully shy person will overnight become an outgoing one or that someone who is passive will discover an as yet untapped vein of assertiveness. In any case, what is most attractive about a person is that part that is most natural and honest. People who give that up in order to make an impression usually look, to everyone except themselves, rather ridiculous.

This is never more clearly seen than in the media, when someone who starts out as an ordinary Joe with a bit of talent suddenly becomes a star. The transformation can be quite alarming and, for the person concerned, a complete disaster. How many such people have you seen start to believe their own publicity and become monsters of egotism? And how many of them then find themselves divorced from the people on whom they used to depend and completely at sea in a world that is utterly false? The numerous stories of pop stars, film stars, sports personalities and others who end up as victims of drink, drugs, depression and even violence are not coincidences. Losing your grip on your personality is a dangerous business.

One change that we all see taking place is the kind that affects people in long-term relationships. It can go either way. You often see couples who, having been together for years, have learned to accommodate each other by moving closer together in terms of personality. Alternatively, it is also quite common to come across people who have been driven apart by years of physical proximity and eventually become completely incompatible. This often leads to the tragic sight of a couple past middle-age and with their children having reached independence deciding to split up after years of barely concealed dislike.

As I mentioned earlier, we spend quite a bit of time constructing compatibility studies for people in relationships that seem to be in trouble. What is quite alarming is the degree to which people believe it is possible to keep their partner's 'good' bits and throw out the 'bad.' The problem is that not only do our tests ignore the sexual attraction in a relationship, they are also forced to leave out love. This is a significant omission but, to the best of my knowledge, there is no reliable test for love on the market. Consequently I spend some of my time looking at relationships that, by all reasonable standards, are never going to work. The plain fact of the matter is that the people in these relationships do, despite my dispassionate analysis of their plight, dote on each other and are looking to me anxiously for some way in which to put the whole situation right. This is the sort of change that, I feel, is not going to be possible, and the quest for it is likely to cause considerable emotional pain to both the partners. We cannot love someone on condition that they become someone else. That seems obvious, but it is quite surprising how often people try to impose some really rather unrealistic changes on each other in order to achieve a partner who is more 'acceptable' to their tastes.

Why use tests?

Although testing has been available for many years, it is only quite recently that it has become widely used. There are a couple of reasons why this is so. The first is the now almost universal availability of small, fast computers that can run complicated testing programs in seconds. Not long ago each test had to be carried out by a chartered psychologist who had to calculate the results by hand. This was time-consuming and therefore very expensive. The data can now be fed into a computer, either by punching numbers in on the keyboard or, increasingly, by using an optical character reader to scan the respondent's answer sheet. The processing takes hardly any time at all, and the report is prepared and printed at the touch of a button. This leaves the psychologist free to concentrate on the interpretation of the results, which is, after all, the clever bit.

In Great Britain another development has made testing more popular. The British Psychological Society has made it possible for people who are not chartered psychologists to take a specialized course in psychometric testing leading to its Certificate of Competence in Occupational Testing. This has created a whole new class of people who are qualified to administer tests and interpret the results. However, as these people are not as highly qualified as a chartered psychologist their time costs less, and consequently the cost of testing has declined.

Greater convenience and cheapness are compelling reasons for the popularity of testing but they are by no means the only ones. The truth is that the old methods of selection are very largely discredited. The interview still has its place as an ancillary to testing, but it is very unreliable. We have all been through interviews. Some of us will have experienced the process from both sides of the table. The applicant makes a shrewd assessment of what the potential employer wants to see and understandably tries to put on the best face possible. If the employer wants a team player, then the applicant will stress team experience; if a rugged individualist is called for, then that is what will appear. On the employer's side there is usually the assumption that the person conducting the interview is a 'good judge of character.' It is amazing just how many people flatter themselves with this title. And yet what too often happens is that the interviewer displays a whole series of foibles, biases, and preferences that the clever applicant will use to their advantage. On the other hand, a perfectly well-qualified applicant who happens to fall foul of one of the interviewer's taboos will fail despite his or her merits. It is perhaps forgivable if an employer picking a personal assistant takes his or her own foibles into account. But all too often the interviewer is actually a manager who will simply send the successful applicant to work in a department where the existing employees might have quite a different set of prejudices.

The advantage of testing is that it does away with both the artifice of the applicant and any signals that the interviewer might pass on about his or her expectations. An effective personality profile really gets inside the head of the applicant and takes a good look at the mental furniture on display. This always sounds rather sinister, but it is not really so. I was once asked to lecture to a group of Oxford University students who would soon be on the job market and were quite likely to be tested. They were anxious about the sort of information that they might let slip when tested. I pointed out that the test would certainly identify whether they were shy or outgoing, suffered from anxiety, were creative or not, and things of that sort. However, it would not reveal if applicants drank too much, loved their mothers, or had a strange fixation about ladies' underwear. I think they found this reassuring.

Testing allows the employer to select staff in a much more professional way than by pure gut feeling. For example, when I was being trained in psychometrics, several of the people on my course were personnel professionals from one of the major motoring organizations. They explained to me that one of their most difficult jobs was recruiting women for telesales, which involved sitting on the phone all day selling motor insurance. For many people a job like this would be torture, but, as in all walks of life, some people are good at it. In fact, some of the employees were so good at it that they exceeded all expectations. The organization set its sales staff targets that were, if they were reasonably efficient, quite easy to achieve. However, some of the women not only hit the target but managed to exceed it by as much 17–20%. These were the queens of the telesales business. The organization tested the personality of these successful sellers and created a norm based purely on the results. Then they tried an interesting experiment. They hired two new groups of women. One group was hired by a mixture of traditional techniques and personality assessment, but the other group was tested and then compared to the group of supersellers. Only those whose profiles matched those of the very successful women were hired. Over a period of 18 months it was discovered that, as you might expect, many of the women selected became disenchanted with the work and left. Others were simply not good enough at selling insurance and were not kept on after their trial period. But of the group that had been selected by comparisons with the supersellers, most had stayed and become supersellers too. This method of selecting 'ideal' staff is becoming increasingly popular. I currently have a client who supplies computer experts to large companies on short-term contracts. His problem is that he has to hire people for a few months and drop them into a large organization where they will immediately represent his company. The importance of getting the right people can hardly be overestimated. First, the people you select must make the right impression in the workplace to which they are sent. Also they must have the right temperament to be able get on with the job in spite of being in an alien environment. As you would expect, there are some people who are ideal for this, and we are busy constructing a norm based on such high performers. But the other part of the job is trying to weed out unsuitable people before they get hired and damage their employer's reputation. To this end we have constructed a 'picture' of a suitable applicant and are able to match people to it with a high degree of success.

What other reasons are there for testing? We have discussed how it helps to get the 'right' people, but what of the wrong ones? Psychologists tend to say that there are no good or bad personalities, and in one sense this is true. However, there are certainly troubled personalities, and if you have one of these on your staff you could be in for a lot of difficulty. We worked with a company that had a sales department staffed by young female clerks. One of them – let's call her Katie – was bright, friendly, outgoing, conscientious and in every way an asset to the office. Eventually she married and moved to another town where her husband had found a job. We were asked to take Katie's profile and use it as a template when selecting a replacement. It is possible to do this in percentage terms so, for example, you might get another applicant who was, say, 95% Katie. Just as we were about to start work on this assignment the management had a change of heart. They decided that without any further testing or interviewing they would put a woman from another department – we'll call her Sophie – into the job. Fortunately, psychometricians spend a great deal of time doing things simply to increase their knowledge, so even though there was no financial incentive, we decided to test Sophie and measure her against Katie's profile. What a shock! This was a girl who was clearly deeply troubled. She was extremely introverted, suffered from huge levels of anxiety, and showed every sign of being emotionally very unstable. Her condition was clearly so serious that we approached her manager and pointed out that this young woman might quite possibly be a suicide risk. When she was invited to discuss what was bothering her it turned out that, as we suspected, she had enormous personal problems at home and had indeed given thought to the possibility of suicide.

It is strange how some people who would never find the time, or perhaps the courage, to go and see a doctor or psychiatrist, have great faith in the ability of a personality profile to reveal their problems. In truth, the sort of questionnaire used for employment purposes is not really designed to reveal medical problems, but in certain circumstances these may come to light. We were approached by two young men who had set themselves up in an insurance brokerage and were doing, by their own account, extremely well. However, they were both very keen to be tested. I couldn't quite see what they were trying to achieve because they were not really very willing to discuss their aims. Even so, we carried out two tests on each of them and discovered a couple of quite disturbing profiles. Whereas Sophie had been withdrawn and unstable, these two were outgoing, extremely tense, driven and absolutely crucified by anxiety. They were clearly what psychologists call Type A personalities. Type A has been called the 'heart attack profile.' This is probably not quite accurate, and later research has suggested that such people are only at increased risk of heart disease if they are also full of suppressed anger. However, it was quite clear that our two young businessmen were living a dangerous lifestyle. The odd part was that when I talked to them it was quite clear that they had suspected some such outcome, and this was the reason they had asked to be tested in the first place. Why not go to a doctor? It seems that ambitious young executives don't think going to the doctor is quite the thing, but filling in a personality questionnaire is absolutely acceptable!

Other people also use testing as a means to sort out their personal problems. One of the services we offer is the compatibility study, in which two people involved in a relationship each complete a personality profile and submit it for a comparative analysis. One thing you cannot do by this method is test for sexual attraction. We have probably all had the experience of being physically attracted to someone we don't much like or, conversely, being very fond of someone but finding them unexciting in a sexual sense. The compatibility study looks at the various dimensions of a personality profile and assesses similarities and differences. We start by looking at what are called the second order factors. These are the big five personality factors that form the bedrock of the personality. They are: extroversion/introversion, anxiety, control, independence and sensitivity. If you find a large difference on one, two, or even more of these dimensions, it does not mean that the relationship is necessarily in trouble. However, the people who approach us for such an analysis are, almost by definition, people who are experiencing difficulties in their relationship, and therefore one can suppose with a fair degree of safety that large differences in personality are at the root of the problem.

Some areas of personality are more crucial to a relationship than others. For example, if one partner is highly creative and the other is not, this is unlikely to be a major source of trouble. It may well be that the less creative partner is at times irritated by the unrealistic notions of the creative one, but, after all, we all get on each other's nerves a bit, don't we?

Take, in contrast, a dimension such as easy-going/controlled. People who score highly on control like protocol and rules. They enjoy the comfortable, uptight feeling they get from moral certitude. High scorers might feel very much at home in rather puritanical religious groups where they could disapprove heartily of the 'out crowd' of sinners and reprobates. People who are high on control sometimes feel that those of a more relaxed demeanour are not merely different but morally reprehensible. On the other hand, people who score low on this dimension may be equally sure that the only way to be is totally laid back, seeing high scorers as uptight, tedious, pompous zealots. Thus a major difference on this dimension could indicate a relationship with significant problems.

The advantage of an analysis of this sort is that it can map out for a couple the psychodynamics of their relationship, which are hard to see clearly from right in the middle of it – especially when there is some kind of battle going on. When you get the whole situation down on paper and take a calm look at it, things can seem much more hopeful. We did an analysis for a couple who, on the face of it, were quite unsuited. The man was highly anxious, temperamental, creative and full of self-doubt. The woman was much calmer and surer of herself but came across as being rather cold and uncaring. Certainly she did not seem like the sort of person her partner could go to with his troubles. It transpired that what he really valued about her was her appearance of calm. He didn't mind that she would not provide sympathy and a shoulder to cry on; he was much more impressed by her calm, unruffled exterior. This, it seems, acted as a great inspiration to him in his many times of crisis, and he later told us that he used to refer to her as 'my Buddha' because of her air of complete serenity.

The thing I like most about psychometric testing is that it doesn't only enable you to help put all the square pegs in square holes and the round pegs in round ones. That's quite a useful thing to do but it's basically fairly banal. The really interesting bit comes when you work, as I do regularly, with a bunch of very highly intelligent and often extremely creative people. This is the real challenge. Not only do you discover that the peg has a completely new and original shape but also that there is a possibility that, once the subject has been made aware of this, he or she may even be able to find a hole that fits or, even better, be able to persuade someone to make a hole just that shape in order to fit him into it. When that happens it is what I call job satisfaction.

Can you cheat?

Many people are keen to know if cheating is possible when you complete a personality profile. The short answer is 'no.' There are no right or wrong answers, and all the tester is trying to do is elicit truthful responses to the questions. When testing is being used for employment selection, the potential employer has, or should have, quite a clear idea of the sort of person they want. If you are not that sort of person then you are unlikely in the long term to be happy in the job, no matter how superficially attractive it may be. But that, of course, is not the whole story. People are often very keen to get a particular job, either because of financial need, or because they think that once they get through the door they will be able to carve a niche for themselves even if they do not conform exactly to what the employer was expecting. Consequently, they try to imagine how the employer wants them to be, and then answer the questions in such a way as to give a favorable impression. This is doomed to failure for several reasons.

Tests are constructed with a built-in lie detector. I won't tell you how this works because that would invalidate many tests and make me extremely unpopular with my colleagues. Suffice to say that if you try to impress the tester by creating a false persona, you will be found out. If you have merely made a minor effort to make yourself seem 'nicer,' then that will be noted but will probably not affect your prospects too much. However, if you are discovered to be the sort of person who tries to pull the wool over the employer's eyes, this will suggest that you would be untrustworthy in other respects and may well lead to your application being rejected.

I was once, rather to my surprise, approached by the head of a religious order (which I will not name for reasons that will become obvious) who asked me to carry out personality tests on himself and his monks. The order was very largely influenced by Americans who appreciate the value of psychometric testing. We contacted members in various parts of the world and got them to complete questionnaires. It was only when we started to process the data that we noticed that every single respondent had an unexpectedly high lie score. With considerable embarrassment I contacted the Vicar General and, using all the tact I could muster, explained the problem. Instead of being furious he was rather amused. He pointed out that monks spend their whole lives trying, as best they can, to imitate Jesus. Naturally they fail, but they keep on trying. In a very special sense and from the highest motives they are living a lie, but in this case, it was a lie that the test had detected with ease.

There is only one field of employment that I know of where people who try to present themselves in a falsely flattering light are smiled upon. Salesmen, especially those who use high-pressure techniques, spend their whole lives trying to convince the public that they are good guys whose word can be believed. There is simply no room in their vocabulary for words like 'honesty' or 'self-doubt.' Imagine a salesman who told you, 'Yes, it's quite a good machine, but our competitors make one just as good that's cheaper.' Unless you are contemplating such a career, ruthless honesty in completing your questionnaire is strongly recommended.

Besides outright attempts to cheat, there are other things that respondents can do that will give a false result. One of them is what I call 'philosophizing.' All the tests I have met work on the principle that the best answer is the one you give 'off the top of your head.' The important point to remember is that the tester is trying to find out how you feel about yourself rather than carry out a police investigation into your life. One test we used contained the statement, 'Most people find me sociable and outgoing.' The respondent was, as usual, invited to agree, disagree or give a 'don't know' answer. Imagine my surprise when one lady wrote to me after the test to say that she had carried out a straw poll among her friends and relatives and then gave a statistically accurate but quite useless answer to the question. Many of the questions in such questionnaires could, if pondered long enough, give considerable food for thought. Even something quite simple, like 'I enjoy going to parties,' could depend very much on your mood, the time of year, your financial circumstances, and a variety of other factors. This is most emphatically not what the tester is concerned with. Most of us can decide as a general principle whether we like parties or not. That is all that the question is trying to establish, and if you complicate matters, you will merely end up giving a rather stilted picture of yourself. Even worse are the respondents who insist on annotating the questionnaire with their thoughts on the questions, their possible meanings, and the variety of answers that they could, in certain circumstances, come up with. Most of these tests are marked by computer and there is simply no facility to input comments like, 'My wife has just left me so I don't feel much like going out this week, but I usually like parties if I know the other guests.' This is not a joke; such comments are quite often included.

Another little trick that respondents come up with is something called 'random responding.' In situations where an employer has decided to test a large number of staff as part of an evaluation exercise, you often find people who resent what they see as an invasion of their privacy. They sometimes seek to protect themselves by simply checking boxes on the answer form at random, in order, they hope, to subvert the system. However, test constructors are on to this dodge and there is a system built into many tests that alerts markers to a random responder.

I have had a rather different experience with unwilling staff. Some of my clients are oil companies, and from time to time they instruct members of staff to take part in team-building exercises. If you are a six-foot-three Texan and you have just spent an arduous shift on the rig, the last thing you need when you come off duty is a personality questionnaire – especially if you were expecting an inch-thick steak instead. Rather than getting their revenge by random responding, some of our clients have found our telephone number on the documents and phoned from the middle of some wind-swept ocean to make their displeasure clear in person. The whole point of personality profiles is to help both the employer and the applicant to find the best possible working relationship. This can only be done effectively if you are honest in your answers. My heart-felt advice to those about to take any kind of personality test is, don't try to cheat.

How are tests made?

Psychologists start with the construction of a theoretical model of personality. From that they decide on various personality dimensions that they are interested in measuring. Let's say that we want to measure extroversion. We might devise questions that we thought would test whether the subject was outgoing, enthusiastic, people-oriented, and impulsive. A very large sample of questions (known as the item pool) is necessary because many of them will eventually be rejected as unsuitable. Once we have our questionnaire we administer it to a large sample of people. It is very important that these people come from as wide a variety of backgrounds as possible, and that various levels of intelligence are represented within the group. The final items for the test will be selected according to a number of criteria. These are: the items must be reliable, they must be valid, and they must discriminate effectively between individuals.

To get reliable items it is important to eliminate any ambiguities either in the items themselves or in the scoring instructions. A famous example of an item that was originally reliable as a measure of extroversion but later became unreliable is the statement: 'I like to go to gay parties.' When the item was written it only examined the respondent's attitude to lively social occasions but, as the language has evolved, it now would also be seen to be a question about sexual orientation. To ensure that the items are presented to each respondent in exactly the same way, whenever a test is used a standardized test booklet is published and a standardized method of test administration is produced in the form of a manual for use by all test administrators. These precautions may seem rather obvious, but they do matter. Psychologists will become very concerned if, for example, a test booklet is redesigned in some way. Unless the effects of any changes are carefully measured, you cannot be sure that the reliability of the test has not been damaged.

When a test is being standardized it will be presented to a large number of people and their results will be carefully analyzed. From these results it is possible to produce norm tables. Each norm will be based on a different sample of people, or population, as it is called. These norms are a very important part of testing. For example, a group of 20-year-old undergraduates will score quite differently from a group of, say, middle-aged solicitors. These different norms will be very useful for a variety of special purposes, but for many occasions we will need a general population norm. Since it is not practical to administer the test to the entire population we have to do the next best thing, which is to test a sample of people that represents the population as a whole. This so-called stratified sample will contain the right proportions of people from different age groups, sexes, geographical locations, intelligence levels, etc. It is quite revealing to take the personality test data from one respondent and process the test according to a number of different norms. Our respondent – let's assume he's a middle-aged man – might seem rather a dull chap when compared to a group of 18-year-olds. He is likely to come out as less extrovert, less socially bold and more cautious, and he might have higher levels of anxiety. However, if we then compared him to a group of senior clergymen, for example, he might take on a livelier appearance.

There is much skill involved in writing the items for a test. One of the first things the writer must do is try to reduce as far as possible the insight that the respondent has into the purpose of the items. This is not done simply for the fun of pulling the wool over the respondent's eyes. If respondents are aware that a particular item is measuring, say, anxiety, then their response will reflect that awareness and may not be totally honest. They may, in effect, tell the tester how they see themselves in terms of anxiety and, since many people are not great judges of their own character, this could introduce serious errors.

Test writers also have to be sure that all their items are as clear and unambiguous as possible. An item that, for example, says, 'Most people think I'm a nice person,' is far too vague to be of use. The term 'nice' has only an approximate meaning and covers a rather large area (for example, it could include 'nice looking' as well as 'kind,' 'generous,' and even 'honest.') If the item says instead, 'Most people think I am kind-hearted,' it has a quite specific meaning.

Items also need to relate to specific behavior. An item that asks, 'Are you creative?' is less useful than one that asks, 'Do you write poetry?' The second item offers specific information that may well reflect upon the respondent's level of creativity.

It is very important that each of the items in a test asks only a single question. An item such as, 'I believe discrimination on the grounds of class and wealth are wrong,' is far too confused. Is it testing attitudes to class, or to wealth, or is it a measure of envy? The item needs to be simplified so that it asks one simple direct question.

Items sometimes try to elicit information about the frequency with which the respondent acts in a certain way. Such questions also need to be specific rather than general. An item asking, 'Do you often suffer from tension headaches,' raises a question over the respondent's definition of the word 'often.' Is once a week 'often,' or twice, or do the headaches have to be daily before they can be described as occurring 'often?' In such circumstances the tester must introduce precise information so that the respondent can answer the question satisfactorily. 'Do you suffer from tension headaches more than once a week' would be a much better item.

One of the most important factors in testing is to try to ensure that respondents give the first answer that comes into their head, and the test instructions should always contain advice to that effect. What the tester needs is an instinctive reaction to a situation that describes the subject's most typical way of behaving in that situation.

Graphology

The most obvious argument in favor of graphology is that, in an amateur sort of way, we all believe in and practice it in our everyday lives. We have no difficulty at all in accepting the idea that someone's personality is reflected in their handwriting and most people could quote examples of friends, relatives and colleagues who express some facet of their personality in this way. We have all seen the large, flamboyant, confident script of the extreme extrovert, and in contrast the tiny writing of the very introverted. When we receive a letter from an unknown individual or from someone we know but from whom we have never had correspondence before, we quite routinely examine the handwriting to see what it can tell us about that person. This, I would suggest, accounts for the great popularity of graphology and for the fact that, in spite of objections from psychologists, it is still quite widely used as a means of assessing personality.

However, even at this stage we have a problem. This sort of 'common-sense graphology' is very limited in what it can tell us. Even if we accept that we can discover personality factors in handwriting, what I have described so far is hardly a complete analysis. What is more, it suffers from the fact that we often project personality factors we expect to see onto the writing. I can give a perfect example of a mistake in analyzing someone's handwriting. At Mensa we spend much of our time assessing intelligence; in particular I get involved on a daily basis with highly intelligent children. One thing that is so common among such children as to be almost a symptom of high intelligence is scruffy, illegible handwriting. Many very bright children are treated as poor scholars by teachers who equate neatness with content. One girl came to us whose IQ was in the top one per cent of the population. Then someone noticed that she had beautiful, neat handwriting. Not only that, but she used a rather ornate italic style that went beyond mere neatness and into the realms of calligraphy. This caused some comment among people who worked with bright children and were all only too aware of the scruffy handwriting syndrome. Could a girl who wrote so neatly really be that bright? It was almost as though a sort of inverted snobbery was beginning to take hold. People were so used to seeing the awful writing of bright kids that they just could not believe that this paragon of neatness could also be clever. Then the mystery was solved. The girl had an English name, but her mother was from the Far East and had made great efforts to teach her daughter this particular neat script. What we were seeing was only half the story.

Another example may also help to point out some of the shortcomings of basic graphology. It is said that people who slope their handwriting to the right are assertive and forceful. This seems quite logical. After all, if you give the impression that your writing is straining at the leash and trying to rush off the page this could be explained by a certain impatience and forcefulness in your personality. However, I write like that and, while not exactly a shrinking violet, I'm pretty sure (and I have psychometric test results to back my judgement) that I am not at the extreme of assertiveness, extroversion, or social boldness. But I was raised in Scotland in the 1950s, and in those days it was considered 'proper' to slope your writing forward at an angle of 60 degrees. This was not allowed to be a matter of personal taste. You had to slope your writing in the approved manner or risk punishment.

Professional graphologists maintain that what I have discussed so far has nothing to do with their work, which, they would argue, is capable of analyzing personality in great depth. I do not have space here to go into a huge amount of detail, but I can give a brief impression of a few of the features a graphologist would look for and the inferences that might be drawn from these. Below are a few things to look for taken from a popular work on the subject.

First, the writing would be examined in order to distinguish the three zones into which it can be divided. These are called the upper, middle, and lower zones and are simply the areas filled by the ascenders, body and descenders of letters. Thus letters like k, l, and b enter the upper zone; c, a, and x occupy the middle zone, and y, j, and g enter the lower zone. Graphology tells us that the upper zone is concerned with intellect and matters of the spirit; the middle zone reveals likes, dislikes and the writer's adaptability to everyday life; and the lower zone expresses the 'foundation of our personality.' I'm not quite sure what this means, but apparently when the lower zone is emphasized 'the practical, material or instinctual side of life is dominant.' People who have large writing are said to be more subjective than objective. They are supposed to be enthusiastic, self-confident and need plenty of space to express themselves. Small writers, on the other hand, may be modest, and do not need as much space for self-expression. Upright writers, apparently, are of a reserved disposition and do not readily show their emotions. Right-slanted writers, on the other hand, show a need to be among people.

The writer goes on like this for many chapters and covers subjects such as form and degree of connection, pressure, stroke, regularity and rhythm, letter formation and speed, and many more. My reaction to all this is, how do they know?

Who told them what the idiosyncrasies of handwriting indicate about personality? Where is the statistical evidence to show that, say, all extroverted people have something in common in their handwriting that helps to identify them? Where is the evidence that people with large writing are 'more subjective than objective' and what, if anything, does that mean?

Graphology does fascinate, but it is also curiously resistant to any scientific form of analysis. One of the problems is that the differences between one handwriting and another are a matter of such a plethora of detail that it is really very difficult to devise a system that can relate all the tiny variations to known personality factors. Maybe one day someone will come up with such a system, but until then graphology will remain an intuitive art, which in talented hands may reveal some useful information but which is not really a reliable means of personality analysis for everyday use.

To enable you to try your own hand at graphology I have obtained a number of handwriting samples from friends and colleagues. These are presented with no clue as to who the authors might be. I have also posed a series of questions for you to consider. If you take graphology seriously, you will at once object that you cannot get some of the information you need (for example, you will have no way of knowing what pressure the writer used). However, the questions do not demand a deep character analysis, and if handwriting really contains clues as to personality, it should be possible to ascertain the answers to the questions by a careful examination of the samples provided.

Study the samples closely and see what you make of them. When you have had a chance to form some opinions you can test your skill by answering the following questions. Don't look at the answers until you have completed all the questions.

A

Guarantees of certainty, safety and success would make trust redundant. Why bother to embark on the adventure of faith if watertight guarantees are handed over at the outset? We have to trust that all shall be well without expecting it to be so.

B

It is spring, moonless night in the small town, starless and bible-black, the cobblestreet silent and the hunched, courters'- and rabbits' wood limping invisible down to the sloeblack, slow, black crowblack, fishing boat-bobbing sea.

C

As requested, here is a sample of my handwriting, which becomes stranger to my eyes the more I use a word processor! Thank heavens you didn't ask me for an essay about my summer holidays, since I'm far too busy planning my future one. I was born with wanderlust, and am heading off to Rome fairly soon (as I hope you'll recall) for some delicious food and coffee, inspiring crumbling ruins, and breathtaking art. Will I be back? Hmmm, we shall see!

D

Fiona,

Just a quick note to say thanks for the lovely meal last night. I spoke to David this morning, who was still dreaming of your wonderful risotto, and he can't wait to come over again. Jane sends her love and tells me to remind you not to forget to feed the cats!

Speak to you soon,

E

Dear Julian

It is with great pleasure that I offer my services to both you and the Mensa Assess Your Personality Book. I trust that my contribution will be well received and find its way into history as part of this well conceived offering to society produced exclusively by Carlton Books

F

If you can keep your head when
                 all about you
are losing theirs and blaming it on you
If you can trust yourselves when all
              men doubt you
But make allowance for their doubting
                                    too.

G

Though brilliantly sunny,
Saturday morning was overcoat
weather again, not just topcoat
weather, as it had been all
week and as everyone hoped
it would stay.

1. Two of the writers follow the same profession. Which are they?

2. One sample is written by someone who spends his life chasing deadlines (and getting others to do the same). Which is it?

3. One sample is written by someone for whom English is a foreign language. Which is it?

4. Pick out all the women writers.

5. One of the writers is a professional author. Which one?

6. Would you say that G is written by a forceful, aggressive personality?

7. Is B an introvert or an extrovert?

8. Would you think of F as quiet and retiring or outgoing and assertive?

9. What conclusions did you come to about the writer of C?

10. Now for a real test! Two of the writers are married to each other. Can you pick them out?

11. Another tough question: one of the writers was originally left-handed but was made to learn to write with the right hand. Which was it?

12. How would you assess the writer of sample E?

Answers

1. A and D are both written by graphic designers.

2. E.

3. B was written by a German.

4. B, C, F.

5. G.

6. No, G is rather quiet.

7. B is rather introverted.

8. F is an outgoing, assertive person.

9. C was written by an American lady who works as an editor in a London publishing company. As you might expect, she has literary tastes and is quite creative. She is easy-going and friendly.

10. G and B.

11. G.

12. E is a forceful personality, hard-driving and quite aggressive, who works in a high-pressure job. People who know him say that he has a softer side, which becomes apparent on closer acquaintance.

Colour analysis

The 1970s were the heyday of color analysis, though it still survives in some places. It was based on the assumption that our color preferences indicate personality traits. Just like graphology, there is a sort of common-sense about this proposition that makes it attractive. We do know that certain colors have an effect on us. Bright colors make us feel happy, drab ones depress us. We even talk of 'warm' and 'cold' colors. I well remember at 17 decorating my bedroom for the first time in what I thought would be an eye-catching combination of blue and brilliant white. The end result was so cold that before long I had to admit I could no longer live with it and redecorated using a somewhat cozier combination.

The use of color to influence mood is well-established in the retail trade. Greengrocers use lighting of a subtle green to make their vegetables look more appetizing, while butchers use a delicate pink light to enhance the appearance of meat. Blue is never used anywhere near food because it makes it look uncanny and unwholesome. People can also appear different in different colored lighting. We know that a soft, warm light makes us look more attractive. Conversely, I went to a university where the authorities thought it the height of modernity to fill the corridors, lecture theatres and seminar rooms with neon strip lighting. The result? Everyone went around looking, and eventually feeling, pale and ill. Psychologists have made a number of discoveries about the effect of color. For example, people deprived of natural light during the winter may suffer from seasonal affective disorder (SAD), a form of depression that can be cured by subjecting the sufferer to regular periods of exposure to a special light that imitates natural light perfectly. It seems that while artificial light replaces the real thing adequately for most purposes, it does not contain the full spectrum of colors present in natural light, and this deficiency is sufficient to cause some people mental disturbance. This can range from a slight feeling of being 'under the weather' to a really incapacitating depression.

Experiments have also been reported in which color has been used to try to influence the mood of highly aggressive people. It is said that a room with a largely pink color scheme has a calming effect and reduces levels of aggression. Again, we have little difficulty in accepting how something like this might work as we have all had the experience of being emotionally stimulated by color.

However, the big question is, can color preferences indicate personality? Assumptions are often made that certain colors are in some way connected with emotions. The most obvious example is that of red, which is thought of as a bold, aggressive, extrovert sort of color. Every so often we read articles in the press in which 'a psychologist' is reported as saying that drivers of red cars have been proved to be more aggressive, more impatient, more status-conscious, and so on. Books have been published that give the most detailed information about the personality implications of certain color choices. It is claimed that once you know which colors someone likes or dislikes you can make accurate predictions about that person's character. But can you?

Just as with graphology, color analysis depends for its effect on assumptions that, while they might appear to be reasonable, are impossible to prove. Though you may well be able to find people with an outgoing, aggressive personality who love the color red, you simply cannot come up with a reliable link between the two things. Our reactions to color are very complicated and, in many cases, influenced by social and cultural considerations. Although you may, by taking note of someone's color preferences, get a general idea of the sort of person they are, it is not possible to devise a system that will tell you accurately about all the components of personality just from color choice.

Face reading

Can you judge personality by someone's face? For many people it is almost an article of faith that they can. There is a widespread belief that, especially as we get older, our experiences are reflected in our facial expression. George Orwell said: 'At 50 everyone has the face he deserves' or, as Oscar Wilde put it, 'A man's face is his autobiography.' People who reckon themselves 'a good judge of character' would maintain that they can just about read the secrets of a person's soul by looking at the face. There are certain signs that are widely regarded as infallible indications of character. For example, someone who does not hold your gaze when you speak to them is regarded as shifty. Interestingly, however, the Chinese regard looking straight into someone's face as rude and see it as a sign that you do not trust the other person: they believe that you are looking for lies.

People whose eyes are set close together are also somewhat suspect but, on the other hand we speak of people having a 'frank, open face' as though the possession of wide-set eyes was in itself an indication of honesty. Beards are also regarded by some as expressing some sort of character defect. The former British Prime Minister, Margaret Thatcher, was noted for her aversion to beards and those who wanted political advancement had to resign themselves to being clean-shaven.

Yet we also know quite well that none of this is particularly credible. Let's think of a few examples. Surely one of the most wicked, bloodthirsty men in history was Joseph Stalin. He was personally responsible for the deaths of millions and dealt not only with political opponents but even people who might possibly have had unreliable political views with the utmost savagery. Yet, before the truth about his regime was discovered, he was a popular figure, especially with Allied troops during the war. His comfortable, kindly appearance led the soldiers to nickname him Uncle Joe. Could anyone have been more wrong about a face? Here's another worrying thought. Compare Stalin's avuncular looks with the wild and wacky features of Trotsky. Which of these men would you regard as the dangerous revolutionary? I would suggest that Trotsky would win that contest any day. Look at that sinister little beard, and the glasses, not to mention the threatening frown. However, as history shows, though Trotsky was indeed a firebrand and revolutionary, he was not even in Stalin's league and was eventually pushed aside and then murdered on the orders of Uncle Joe.

Brighten up your diet with a weekly
box of seasonal organic veg!

How to use
this voucher

Go to www.abelandcole.co.uk/amazon,
choose one of our fruit and veg boxes
and add it to your basket.

Enter the code 〈**BATWIZLL**〉 at the checkout and
place your order. Pop the kettle on, and your feet up.

You'll get your FREE cookbook on your 1st delivery,
and your 4th box FREE with a FREE big bottle
of Extra Virgin Olive Oil (750ml).

Give us a ring on 08452 62 62 62
if you have any questions at all.

graze®.com
Snacking | REINVENTED

TRY A FREE GRAZE BOX

I'm from a sustainable forest, biodegradable & 100% recyclable

We believe that getting your hands on good snacks should be as easy as putting your hand in the biscuit tin. So our snack inventors have created over **100 tasty nibbles** to deliver to you. Go to **graze.com** and use your special code to try them **FREE.**

Tear and share your special **FREE** box vouchers

1 Here's how to get hold of your **FREE** first box
Visit us at:
www.graze.com

2 enter your special code:
FRIEND0214

3 we'll post you your **FREE** box
For new UK customers only. Valid credit or debit card required but your first box is free & you can stop deliveries easily online or at any time. Ts & Cs at graze.com/uk/help/terms.

FREE box code...
FRIEND0214
graze.com

1 Here's how to get hold of your **FREE** first box
Visit us at:
www.graze.com

2 enter your special code:
YOUR0214

3 we'll post you your **FREE** box
For new UK customers only. Valid credit or debit card required but your first box is free & you can stop deliveries easily online or at any time. Ts & Cs at graze.com/uk/help/terms.

FREE box code...
YOUR0214
graze.com

GET YOUR ✦FREE✦ BOX OF BETTER SNACKS BY POST

TRY A FREE GRAZE BOX

graze.com
Snacking REINVENTED

choose from over **100** tasty snacks

Tear and share your special **FREE** box vouchers

your special code: **YOUR0214**

graze.com
snacking REINVENTED

one **FREE** graze box for you

your special code: **FRIEND0214**

graze.com
snacking REINVENTED

one **FREE** graze box for a friend

It is not hard to think of other examples. What about Saddam Hussein, the former Iraqi dictator? Imagine for a moment that you had heard nothing about the invasion of Kuwait, the gassing of Kurdish villagers, the Gulf Wars, or the terror tactics he used on his own people. Just look at his face. It would not be at all hard to see him as a nice guy. Look at those wide-set eyes, the open face, and that expression, could it not be thought of as stern but kindly? Is there anything in that face that would really make you think of this man as a ruthless killer? Remember, many of his own countrymen were quite convinced that he is a fine leader of the nation. And they were looking at exactly the same face as you.

Unfortunately, our judgments are too often based on rather silly prejudices. It is, for example, no accident that people of light coloring are known as 'fair.' The American Heritage Dictionary of

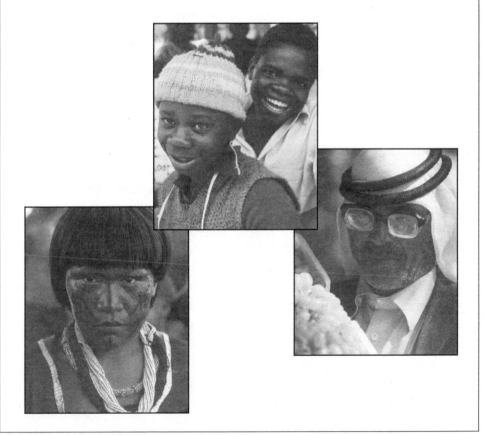

the English Language gives these as its first two definitions of the word 'fair':

1. Of pleasing appearance, especially because of a pure or fresh quality; comely.
2. a. Light in color, especially blond: fair hair.
   b. Of light complexion: fair skin.

On the other hand, dark-haired women are known as 'brunette.' Look that word up in a thesaurus and you will find it linked to words like 'somber' and 'gloomy.' Do you find all your dark-haired friends and acquaintances somber or gloomy? Of course not, yet the stereotype remains and affects the way people regard each other, especially when they are making snap judgements on people they do not really know well.

It does not take much thought to come up with people who have faces that are not what is commonly regarded as open, honest or kindly but whose actions belie this initial impression. Think, for example, of the rumpled detective Columbo, played by Peter Falk. This man is not only of swarthy appearance, but has a glass eye, dresses in scruffy, ill-fitting clothes, and smokes cheap cigars. Yet we know from first acquaintance that Columbo is to be regarded as a sympathetic character who we can trust much more than all the smoothies who try to outwit him with their dastardly plots. Of course, Columbo is only a fictional character, but does that matter? If anything, it makes our impressions more important. After all, filmmakers have a very limited time in which to convey to us aspects of a character's personality. They have to use subtle visual clues to let the audience know what is going on. Strangely, in fiction there is a tradition of characters who look strange or unpleasant but who turn out to be heroes. We can think immediately of Quasimodo, who terrifies everyone, including Esmeralda, with his extreme ugliness but is ultimately shown to be both kind and brave, or Beauty and the Beast where the handsome prince's true nobility of character is hidden by his beastly appearance. In real life, we are far less likely to look for beauty of character behind physical ugliness.

Research has been carried out that shows how facial blemishes are regarded by some as a sign that the unfortunate possessor is in some way responsible for the misfortune. People with artificial scars were instructed to frequent public places and the reactions of those with whom they came in contact were closely observed. It was seen quite clearly that people tended to avoid those who were disfigured even if the blemish was really quite minor. Where the victim was a woman the tendency to shun her was even more marked. What people seem to be most attracted by are even, regular features. Men might get away with being craggily handsome but, on the whole, the nearer you conform to what is popularly thought of as 'good-looking,' the more likely you are to be perceived as honest and trustworthy. It is interesting to what extent the features that excite greatest approval are those that are exhibited best by the very young. There is one particular feature of human response that is

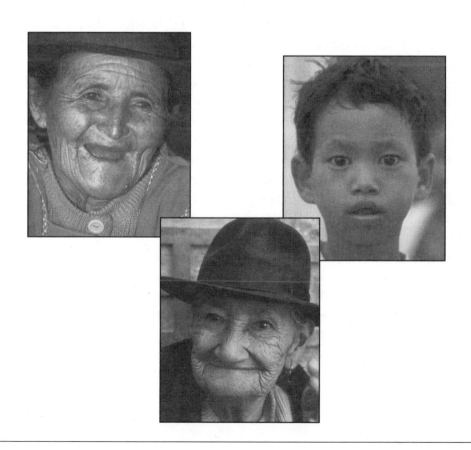

very relevant here. People are very strongly programmed to respond in a protective way to the young. What is very strange is this: many species (though by no means all) will be protective of their own young, but a much smaller number will be protective of the young of other members of their species (for example, a chimpanzee might well defend another chimpanzee's young from a marauding leopard.) The thing that is unique to humans is that they respond in this way to the young of nearly all species.

These young animals have a number of things in common. The size of the eyes in proportion to the rest of the face is much greater in younger animals, as is the size of the head in proportion to the rest of the body. The skin of the young is fresh and unwrinkled and the body is more likely to be slender. The face will tend to be less mobile and will not bear the telltale marks left by years of experience. It has been noted many times that women noted for their beauty usually display these 'infantile' features. Think of a few supermodels, say, Kate Moss, Claudia Schiffer, Naomi Campbell, and you will get the idea. On top of these basic prejudices we have a layer of anecdotal evidence. The problem is that too often our judgements on what sort of face someone has are clouded by a certain amount of knowledge about their character. People just knew that ex-President Nixon was up to no good. But then he was a politician and therefore a certain amount of duplicity was only to be expected (though admittedly he managed it on a grand scale). But supposing he had been your local grocer, or garage owner, would you still have looked at that jowly face and the permanent five o'clock shadow and thought, 'There's a guy who's going to fiddle my bill if I don't watch him?' Possibly not.

As a method of personality assessment face watching at least has huge entertainment value and, at best, you may be able to pick up tiny give-away facial ticks that indicate secret thoughts. However, just as with graphology or color analysis, there is no reliable way in which an assessment of facial features can be rigorously analyzed.

About the tests

Having read something of the background to personality assessment, I hope that you will be interested in discovering more for yourself. The first part of this book was a serious attempt to explain how psychometric personality tests are constructed and used. This section is intended for fun and games. Let's be plain. Personality assessment is so much a part of everyday life that it would be absurdly arrogant to try to maintain it as the exclusive preserve of psychologists. People do it all the time. Whenever people meet each other for the first time, they make an instant personality judgement. That judgement requires no permission or advice from a psychologist, and what's more, there is frequently no appeal against it by the person who is being judged. It is likely that the person forming the opinion will keep it strictly private and will reveal it, if at all, only to close friends or colleagues.

This process will depend almost entirely on intuition backed up, perhaps, by a few facts that happen to be available. The evidence will often be incomplete and the judgement summary but, like it or not, this is the way that the vast majority of personality assessments are actually carried out. And the truth is that some people are good judges of character. Not, of course, nearly as many as actually award themselves that accolade, but there are people who do have an intuitive feel for what makes others tick. How do they do it? Usually they are pretty vague about the process, they say it's 'just a feeling' or 'a matter of experience.' My father would mutter mysteriously, 'Wait till you're as old as I am and then you'll know.' Now that I am as old as he was then, I find I use a computer and psychometric questionnaires. Not, I am sure, what he had in mind.

Self-discovery and the analysis of others are things we do partly from necessity and partly because people find this kind of stuff amusing and fun. And why not? As long as you are not using the results of your analysis for some serious purpose such as staff selection, you are entitled to judge others in whatever way you find best. And be sure they will return the compliment.

The following section contains a number of tests, exercises and games that you can try out. However, before you do so you must be quite clear on one point. These are not psychometric tests. As I hope will have become clear in the first section of the book, such tests are administered only under controlled conditions and by trained staff. The results of psychometric personality tests need to be assessed and communicated to the respondent by someone trained in psychology. Since it is not possible to fulfil these conditions in a book, I am unable to offer you fully standardized psychometric tests. What follows should be regarded as for interest and amusement. But that does not mean it has no value. People are incorrigible in their desire to pry into each others' psyches and it can be not only fun but also quite revealing. Try out some of these games and tests with your friends. You will not necessarily find that they provide you with a detailed personality assessment but they can provide interesting information that will give you plenty of material for discussion.

Before we launch into the actual tests we should just pause to consider one issue: what is intuition? There are at least two answers, one I feel comfortable with and the other I don't. The first is that humans are adept at picking up from each other all sorts of minute signals. Some of these are verbal but may not be contained in the actual text of what someone says to us. We have all had the experience of dealing with people with whom it is advisable to 'read between the lines' even when the message is a spoken one. They have a habit of using slight inflections of speech or subtleties of wording to convey messages that are different from the overt sense of what they are saying. It is even possible to convey a message that is almost the opposite from the overtly spoken one. Many readers will have had the experience of having someone accept an invitation in a tone that lets you know the recipient won't be coming. We have all heard people giving thanks for a Christmas present they did not want in tones that make the disappointment clear while the words preserve the necessary superficial courtesies.

These matters go much deeper than speech. We all give out subliminal signals to each other that indicate how we feel without having to express these feelings in words. Sometimes the signals are intended to convey the subliminal message, but on other occasions they actually betray a feeling that someone would not like to display openly. It is not uncommon to see people give themselves away with a small grimace reflecting a thought that was not intended for public consumption. One such moment I cherish was when General Videla, the former Argentinean military dictator, was officiating at the start of an important international football match in which his country was competing. The arrangements were going badly wrong, and to make matters worse the band was making a bit of a mess of the national anthem. The TV cameras accidentally caught the general at a moment when he was off guard. He was not making furious faces or gesticulating wildly at his aides, but with one tiny flick of an eyebrow he indicated for anyone who happened to notice that someone was going to be in big trouble the next day.

Being alert to these tiny signals is what I call intuition, and it is a very valuable human attribute that we would do well to cultivate. The type of intuition I do not accept is the supernatural sort. Some people would like us to believe that intuition is really a sort of extra sensory perception by which they can gain access to secret information hidden from the rest of us. This, I believe, is nonsense. They are simply unaware that the information is not coming to them through mystical means but is being picked up, probably quite unconsciously, from small but unquestionably physical and verbal signals.

As we have looked at the entire field of personality testing, including some of the more unconventional means that have been employed, it seems a good idea to let you have a look at a variety of methods, including graphology, color analysis and face reading. Although I have no faith in such methods as a means of formal, detailed, systematic personality analysis, it is quite possible that, in the hands of people whose intuitive faculties are highly developed, they may be useful for some purposes. If you look at the section on graphology you will get some hints as to how the (largely self-appointed) experts do it, but you may find that you do just as well trying your own methods.

I have also included questionnaires that are similar in form and presentation to the sort of psychometric tests currently used for personnel selection, and I have provided analysis that is similar to the sort of thing that a real psychometric test might reveal. However, I have also looked at issues that are not normally covered by psychometric testing, such as happiness, fulfilment, sense of humor, and religious conviction. These are all important elements of the human personality, but because they have little direct relevance to either health or employment, they have been widely neglected by psychologists.

Test **One**

Are you in control?

Focus of control is something psychologists are very interested in when they assess personality, but what on earth is it? It sounds a bit like one of those bones in the inner ear that you didn't know you had. However, as far as personality is concerned, locus plays a vital role. Put simply, it decides who is in the driving seat of your life. Your locus can be internal, external or somewhere between the two, but its position will dramatically affect both your personality and your relationships. To find out where your locus of control is and what this means, answer the questions below and then read the explanation at the end of the quiz.

Mark each of the following statements on a scale of 1 to 5 where
1 = Strongly agree, 2 = Agree, 3 = Not sure,
4 = Disagree, and 5 = Strongly disagree.

							score
1.	I am the captain of my ship.	1	2	3	4	5	
2.	You can't fight City Hall.	1	2	3	4	5	
3.	Government is there to solve our problems.	1	2	3	4	5	
4.	I can achieve anything if I try hard enough.	1	2	3	4	5	
5.	I seldom admit defeat.	1	2	3	4	5	
6.	I do not believe in free will.	1	2	3	4	5	
7.	Fate plays an important part in my life.	1	2	3	4	5	
8.	I prefer to fight my own battles.	1	2	3	4	5	
9.	Issues in the modern world are often too complex to understand fully.	1	2	3	4	5	
10.	I sometimes feel unable to cope.	1	2	3	4	5	
11.	At work I like to be told exactly what to do.	1	2	3	4	5	
12.	I would like to conduct an orchestra.	1	2	3	4	5	
13.	Astrology has a profound influence on our lives.	1	2	3	4	5	
14.	I frequently pray over my problems.	1	2	3	4	5	

						score
15. I like to be left to get on with things.	1	2	3	4	5	
16. I am confident about the course my life is taking.	1	2	3	4	5	
17. Destiny plays no part in my life.	1	2	3	4	5	
18. Taking orders irritates me.	1	2	3	4	5	
19. I defer to my elders and betters.	1	2	3	4	5	
20. If you want something done properly, you have to do it yourself.	1	2	3	4	5	
21. We often need help and advice from our superiors.	1	2	3	4	5	
22. I like to be part of an organization.	1	2	3	4	5	
23. I admire cats for their independence.	1	2	3	4	5	
24. I enjoy working independently.	1	2	3	4	5	
25. I like someone else to check my work before it's finished.	1	2	3	4	5	

For questions 1, 4, 5, 8, 12, 15, 16, 17, 18, 20, 23, and 24, give yourself 5 points for answer 1 (strongly agree), down to 1 point for answer 5 (strongly disagree). For questions 2, 3, 6, 7, 9, 10, 11, 13, 14, 19, 21, 22, and 25, give yourself 1 point for answer 1 (strongly agree), up to 5 points for answer 5 (strongly disagree). Maximum score is 125.

Scoring

People with an internal locus believe that they are in charge of their own lives, are frequently optimists, and believe that they can overcome any obstacles. They tend to put very little faith in outside influences or regulating bodies such as governments, or more nebulous concepts such as luck or fate. By contrast, people who feel their lives are controlled by outside forces and that they are powerless to influence events are said to have an external locus; this is associated with a pessimistic attitude to life. In our test, the higher your score, the more internalized your locus.

Over 110

This shows you have a strongly internal locus. You are certainly not lacking confidence in yourself! But beware, you may overestimate your ability to influence your circumstances.

96–110

You're pretty sure that you can control your life but are realistic enough to know that some situations are beyond your control. Your optimism helps you overcome difficulties, and you're wise enough to know when to give up.

75–95

You are inclined to think you have things under control but you have some serious doubts. You are aware that there are times when you feel overcome by events. You are optimistic but easily dented by harsh reality.

61–74

You seriously doubt your ability to handle events and suspect that much of your life is beyond your control. Any optimistic feelings you have are very fragile indeed, and you are uncomfortably aware that you often fail.

46–60

You have a rather pessimistic outlook and feel that most of the time you are controlled by events rather than vice versa. You would like to be more in control but have little confidence that you could bring it off.

31–45

Your lack of confidence in your ability is a serious obstacle to you. It would certainly be worth trying to cultivate a more positive, confident attitude in order to exercise control over many events in your life.

Below 31

Your locus of control is almost entirely external. This is a situation that requires some form of help. Your lack of confidence in your ability is so pronounced that it is adversely affecting your whole life. You really do need to be helped to see that you are not as powerless as you believe yourself to be.

Test Two

Are you anxious?

Are you a bundle of worries? Do you wake up in the night and find that ordinary, everyday problems have become magnified into terrifying insoluble dilemmas? Most of us go through periods of this sort of anxiety but for some people it is a permanent state. Yet others, the lucky few, are able to sail through life concentrating only on the problems of the moment and never giving a thought to the future. The trouble with anxiety is that it can be really debilitating. At the least it may cause mild problems such as sleeplessness and tension headaches, but if it gets out of hand it can cause much more serious problems. Also it makes you feel just awful. Why not answer the questions in this test and see just what level of anxiety you have right now.

You are faced with a number of problems at work. Do you:

		score
a.	Go to sleep as soon as your head hits the pillow.	
b.	Lie awake half the night worrying.	
c.	Think about work for a while before going to sleep.	

You are going on holiday. Do you:

a.	Plan well ahead so you don't have to rush around just before you set off.	
b.	Rush around the day before you go, trying to get everything done in time.	
c.	Check all the bags in a frenzy, panicking in case you have forgotten something essential.	

You have an important interview coming up. Do you:

a.	Look forward to it as you enjoy interviews.	
b.	Have a tense feeling in your stomach all day and can't think of anything else.	
c.	Get on with your work as usual but feel slightly apprehensive about the forthcoming meeting.	

You are holding a dinner party and your guests are late. Do you:

a.	Get in a panic because the dinner might be spoiled.	
b.	Put the dinner on hold and sit down and relax with a drink and a magazine.	
c.	Try to keep the dinner going but feel you cannot really relax until the guests get there.	

Christmas is coming up and lot of things are still left to be done. Do you:

score

5

a.	Take things in your stride and await the holiday with enthusiasm.	
b.	Lie awake at night worrying about how you can possibly get everything done in time.	
c.	Run around like a headless chicken trying to do three things at once.	

You are on your way to a business meeting and get stuck in a traffic jam. Do you:

6

a.	Wait calmly until it moves – after all it's not your fault that you're late.	
b.	Get rather impatient but pass the time by reading your newspaper.	
c.	Get totally overwrought and don't know how to curb your impatience.	

Your next-door neighbors are playing loud music. Do you:

7

a.	Take it calmly and think if it carries on you might have a quiet word with them.	
b.	Get irritated and tell your partner you cannot possibly function with this noise going on.	
c.	Try to ignore it for an hour, then when you can't stand it any longer go next door shouting, 'Turn the music down!'	

You are invited to a large party in the evening. Do you:

score

a.	Look forward to it, as you love meeting new people.	
b.	Rush around all afternoon, trying to prepare but dreading the event.	
c.	Carry on as normal but think it will probably be less trouble to stick with the people you know during the evening.	

You are flying abroad on business. Do you:

a.	Leave two hours early and worry constantly that you might not get there in time.	
b.	Leave in good time but feel slightly apprehensive at the prospect of the journey.	
c.	Take the journey in a relaxed mood as nothing is likely to go wrong.	

You come home and the living room is a total mess. Do you:

a.	Get irritated by it and shout at everybody to tidy it up immediately.	
b.	Sit down with a cup of tea first, but decide to tidy it up before settling down for the evening.	
c.	Leave it, as you are not bothered by living in a mess.	

You are involved in a minor road accident and your car gets dented. Do you:

a.	Calmly exchange insurance details with the other driver and make a mental note of the circumstances of the accident.	
b.	Take a note of the other driver's details with shaky hands.	
c.	Fail to do any of the things necessary as you are far too shaken by the accident.	

You have just completed an examination. Do you: **score**

a.	Forget about it as soon as you get home as the results will not be out for another three months.	
b.	Check a few points when you get home and then lay it to rest.	
c.	Keep thinking about it for some time and wonder how you could have done better.	

You have said something embarrassing among a group of friends. Do you:

a.	Forget about it as soon as you leave.	
b.	Keep thinking about it but accept that it's too late to worry.	
c.	Lie awake worrying all night.	

Some friends have announced they are coming to stay for the weekend. Do you:

a.	Feel excited and plan the weekend ahead with enthusiasm.	
b.	Look forward to the weekend but feel rather nervous about whether it will go all right.	
c.	Dread the weekend and think you'll never manage to get everything ready.	

You're looking for a book that seems to have been misplaced. Do you:

a.	Get irritable and can't relax unless you find the book.	
b.	Keep looking for the book until you have found it.	
c.	Stay calm and decide to look for the book when you've got the time.	

You are out shopping and seem to have lost your credit card wallet. Do you:

score

a.	Remain calm and enquire at all the shops whether the cards have been found before telephoning the bank.	
b.	Dash home in a panic to tell your family of the disaster.	
c.	Phone the credit card company to ask what to do.	

16

You are completing an urgent piece of work on your computer when the power goes off. Do you:

a.	Take it calmly – you back up your work frequently anyway.	
b.	Lose your temper – it's two hours' work wasted.	
c.	Shrug your shoulders and start again.	

17

You look in the mirror and notice you have put on a lot of weight. Do you:

a.	Go on a strict diet and book a course at the gym.	
b.	Relax – your family have always been big.	
c.	Decide to be a bit more careful what you eat.	

18

You are about to go into town and your usual bus has been cancelled. Do you:

a.	Think, 'Not to worry, there'll be another one soon.'	
b.	Worry that you'll be late.	
c.	Feel irritated but realize there's nothing you can do.	

19

While driving you witness a road accident. Do you:

score

a.	See if anyone is injured, then phone the emergency services.	
b.	Rush around in a panic until help arrives.	
c.	Ask passers-by if they will help.	

20

You are suffering from aches and pains the origin of which you are unsure of. Do you:

a.	Assume that it's a minor problem that will clear up of its own accord.	
b.	Assume you have a serious disease and rush to the doctor.	
c.	Decide to wait and see if your symptoms get worse before taking any action.	

21

A friend turns up unexpectedly for the afternoon. Do you:

a.	Drop what you're doing and enjoy his/her company.	
b.	Worry that you will not get your work done.	
c.	Decide to enjoy the social occasion because you can catch up on work later.	

22

You have been called to see your boss for a talk this afternoon and don't know what it's about. Do you:

a.	Assume you're being promoted.	
b.	Assume you're in trouble.	
c.	Assume nothing and wait to see what happens.	

23

You are cooking a dinner for a few friends and realize you have forgotten to buy an important ingredient. Do you:

24

		score
a.	Decide that the whole meal is now ruined.	
b.	Decide that no one will notice the oversight.	
c.	Try to replace the ingredient with something different.	

You have arranged to meet a friend at an agreed place and seem to have lost your way. Time is running out. Do you:

25

a.	Ask a passer-by for directions.	
b.	Calmly assess where you are and try to decide what route to take.	
c.	Get flustered and rush on madly with little idea of where you are going.	

Scoring

For each answer score the number of points indicated.

1.	a:1, b:3, c:2	10.	a:3, b:2, c:1	19.	a:1, b:3, c:2
2	a:1, b:2, c:3	11.	a:1, b:2, c:3	20.	a:1, b:3, c:2
3.	a:1, b:3, c:2	12.	a:1, b:2, c:3	21.	a:1, b:3, c:2
4.	a:3, b:1, c:2	13.	a:1, b:2, c:3	22.	a:1, b:3, c:2
5.	a:1, b:2, c:3	14.	a:1, b:2, c:3	23.	a:1, b:3, c:2
6.	a:1, b:2, c:3	15.	a:3, b:2, c:1	24.	a:3, b:1, c:2
7.	a:1, b:3, c:2	16.	a:1, b:3, c:2	25.	a:1, b:2, c:3
8.	a:1, b:3, c:2	17.	a:1, b:3, c:2		
9.	a:3, b:2, c:1	18.	a:3, b:1, c:2		

The maximum score is 75. If you scored over 65, you are a very anxious person indeed. You should seriously consider ways to calm down and take things more easily. If you scored over 50 but below 65, you are inclined to worry but do not let it get out of control. A score in the 40s suggests average levels of anxiety (most of the population score in this range.) If you scored in the 30s, you are really not much of a worrier at all. A score below 30 would suggest that you are very relaxed, perhaps to the extent that you do not worry much even about things that should probably concern you.

Test Three

Are you optimistic?

Are you an optimist or a pessimist? Do you always carry an
umbrella when you go out? Do you just know that things are going
to go wrong, or is your life one long round of sunny expectation?
Do you assume that things will always turn out all right in the end?
Try the following quiz to see how you measure up as an optimist.

1 Do you lock away your valuables when you go away on holiday?

score [ ]

    a. Always.   **b.** Usually.   **c.** Never.

2 If you lost your keys in the supermarket, would you expect them to be returned?

score [ ]

    a. No.   **b.** I'd hope so.   **c.** Of course.

3 Do you believe that your luck will change for the better?

score [ ]

    a. Never.   **b.** Sometimes.   **c.** Always.

4 When the phone rings, do you usually expect bad news?

score [ ]

    a. Yes.   **b.** No.   **c.** Sometimes.

5 Do you buy shares for speculation?

score [ ]

    a. Frequently.   **b.** Seldom.   **c.** Never.

6 Do you believe that the next year will bring success to you?

score [ ]

    a. Yes.   **b.** No.   **c.** Don't know.

7 Do you believe the future will be rosy?

score [ ]

    a. No.   **b.** Yes.   **c.** Don't know.

8 Do you think that most people are honest?

score [ ]

    a. No.   **b.** Don't know.   **c.** Yes.

9 Would you trust an ex-convict?

    a. Not sure.   **b.** No.   **c.** Yes.

10 If it's raining, do you think that it will soon stop?

    a. Usually.   **b.** Sometimes.   **c.** Never.

11 Do you believe that one day you will win the lottery?

    a. No.   **b.** Yes.   **c.** Not sure.

12 Do you expect to lose some luggage on a long plane flight?

    a. Yes.   **b.** Uncertain.   **c.** No.

13 Do you bet on horses?

    a. Never.   **b.** Sometimes.   **c.** Often.

14 Do you consider yourself lucky?

    a. Usually.   **b.** Sometimes.   **c.** Seldom

15 If you trod on a nail, would you expect it to pierce your foot?

    a. Yes.   **b.** No.   **c.** Not sure.

16 If you played darts with a friend, would you expect to win?

    a. Perhaps.   **b.** No.   **c.** Yes.

17 Do you expect your new outfit to be a success?

a. Always.   **b.** Sometimes.   **c.** Never.

score ☐

18 Do you expect to be sick on a boat?

a. Never.   **b.** Always.   **c.** Sometimes.

score ☐

19 Do you expect it to rain when you play sports?

a. Sometimes.   **b.** Never.   **c.** Always.

score ☐

20 Do you expect a burst pipe at some time in winter?

a. Yes.   **b.** No.   **c.** Don't know.

score ☐

21 If you have a glass of beer of which half has been consumed, do you consider it to be half empty?

a. No.   **b.** Yes.   **c.** Uncertain.

score ☐

22 If you had a flat tire, would you hope that somebody would stop and help?

a. Not sure.   **b.** Yes.   **c.** No.

score ☐

23 Do you expect promotion at work?

a. Yes.   **b.** Not sure.   **c.** No.

score ☐

24 If it's cloudy and cold do you expect snow?

a. Usually.   **b.** Sometimes.   **c.** Never.

score ☐

25 When you plan a barbecue, do you expect it to rain?

a. Yes.   **b.** No.   **c.** Sometimes.

26 Do you think that your position at work will improve?

    a. Not sure.   **b.** No.   **c.** Yes.

27 Do you carry an umbrella in winter?

    a. Always.   **b.** Sometimes.   **c.** Never.

28 Do you save for a rainy day?

    a. Always.   **b.** Never thought   **c.** A bit.
                     of it.

29 If you car fails to start do you expect a serious defect?

    a. Yes.   **b.** Not sure.   **c.** No.

30 Do you expect to win at bingo?

    a. No.   **b.** Yes.   **c.** Not sure.

31 Have you a large life insurance policy?

    a. Yes.   **b.** I have no policy.   **c.** Just a small one.

32 Do you expect to pass every examination?

    a. No.   **b.** Mostly.   **c.** Yes.

33 If you have an illness, do you expect to recover quickly?

    a. Usually.   **b.** Sometimes.   **c.** No.

34 Do you expect your bus to be late?

    a. Always.   **b.** Sometimes.   **c.** Never.

35 Would you select a horse in a race by sticking a pin in a list at random?

 a. Of course. **b.** By no means. **c.** I might do.

36 In winter do you always carry a spade in your car?

 a. Never. **b.** Sometimes. **c.** Always.

37 Do you buy raffle tickets?

 a. Often. **b.** Never. **c.** Occasionally.

38 Do you consider that you are more often lucky than unlucky?

 a. Yes. **b.** No. **c.** Not sure.

39 Would you take in a stray dog?

 a. Yes. **b.** No. **c.** Not sure.

40 Would you eat a dish that you had never tried before?

 a. Yes. **b.** Not sure. **c.** Probably not.

41 Did you celebrate the millennium?

 a. Yes. **b.** No. **c.** Unsure.

42 Do you carry a lucky charm?

 a. Never. **b.** Always. **c.** Sometimes.

43 Are you anticipating a large bonus?

    a. Unsure.   **b.** No.   **c.** Yes.

44 Do you expect it to rain on your holiday?

    a. Never. **b.** Sometimes. **c.** Always.

45 Do you expect to be made redundant this year?

    a. Yes.   **b.** No.   **c.** Unsure.

46 Do you expect the football team that you support will have a good season?

    a. Of course.   **b.** Probably not.   **c.** I don't know

47 Would you trust a complete stranger?

    a. Maybe.   **b.** No.   **c.** Yes.

48 Do you pay a large sum into a pension fund?

    a. Yes.   **b.** No.   **c.** I only have a small pension.

49 If you drop some money, do you expect to find it all?

    a. Of course.   **b.** Probably not.   **c.** Unsure.

50 When you plant bulbs, do you expect them all to flower?

    a. Yes.   **b.** Not sure.   **c.** Probably not.

Scoring

For each answer score the number of points indicated.

1.	a:1, b:2, c:3	14.	a:3, b:2, c:1	27.	a:1, b:2, c:3	40.	a:3, b:2, c:1
2.	a:1, b:2, c:3	15.	a:1, b:3, c:2	28.	a:1, b:3, c:2	41.	a:3, b:1, c:2
3.	a:1, b:2, c:3	16.	a:2, b:1, c:3	29.	a:1, b:2, c:3	42.	a:1, b:3, c:2
4.	a:1, b:3, c:2	17.	a:3, b:2, c:1	30.	a:1, b:3, c:2	43.	a:2, b:1, c:3
5.	a:3, b:2, c:1	18.	a:3, b:1, c:2	31.	a:1, b:3, c:2	44.	a:3, b:2, c:1
6.	a:3, b:1, c:2	19.	a:2, b:3, c:1	32.	a:1, b:2, c:3	45.	a:1, b:3, c:2
7.	a:1, b:3, c:2	20.	a:1, b:3, c:2	33.	a:3, b:2, c:1	46.	a:3, b:1, c:2
8.	a:1, b:2, c:3	21.	a:3, b:1, c:2	34.	a:1, b:2, c:3	47.	a:2, b:1, c:3
9.	a:2, c:1, c:3	22.	a:2, b:3, c:1	35.	a:3, b:1, c:2	48.	a:3, b:1, c:2
10.	a:3, b:2, c:1	23.	a:3, b:2, c:1	36.	a:3, b:2, c:1	49.	a:3, b:1, c:2
11.	a:1, b:3, c:2	24.	a:1, b:2, c:3	37.	a:3, b:1, c:2	50.	a:3, b:2, c:1
12.	a:1, b:2, c:3	25.	a:1, b:3, c:2	38.	a:3, b:1, c:2		
13.	a:1, b:2, c:3	26.	a:2, b:1, c:3	39.	a:3, b:1, c:2		

The maximum score is 150. If you scored over 125, you must be in a permanent, and enviable, state of optimism. You look at the world through rose-tinted glasses, and it never occurs to you that things could turn out badly. Even when you do suffer the odd reversal, you consider it a temporary mishap in your otherwise fortunate life. Living with you must be a strain.

If you scored between 100 and 124, you are still a pretty optimistic kind of person, and your world view is generally warm and pleasantly comfortable. You are aware that life may have its bad patches, but on the whole you don't expect such things to happen to you.

If you scored from 75 to 99, you are quite balanced in your outlook. You don't expect too much of life, but on the other hand you're not exactly gloomy either. Most people will probably score in this range.

If you scored from 60 to 74, you are rather pessimistic. You don't expect your life to be easy, and feel that on the whole if things can go wrong, they will.

If you scored below 60, why bother to get out of bed? Your life is not worth living and you never really thought that it would be.

Test Four

Are you intuitive?

Intuition is a faculty that causes intense disagreement between those
who believe strongly in it and those who don't. Jung regarded it
as an important function of the human mind, and many thousands
of people who 'feel' their way through life would agree with him.
Opposed to them are those who think there is no substitute for
hard facts and cold logic and that so-called intuition is just a lot
of nonsense. Which type are you? The following questions should
give you a pretty good idea of your orientation. Try to answer each
question without hesitation. If you have to think before you answer,
that in itself will tell you something about whether you are intuitive
or logical!

		score
1	Do you usually win at gambling? Yes (B) No (A)	
2	Do you trust your feelings even when they seem to be irrational? Yes (B) No (A)	
3	Do you like to look beneath the surface of human relationships? Yes (B) No (A)	
4	Have you ever used a ouija board? Yes (B) No (A)	
5	Are you superstitious? Yes (B) No (A)	
6	Do you feel that certain places have an 'atmosphere'? Yes (B) No (A)	
7	Do you usually win at guessing games? Yes (B) No (A)	
8	Do you sometimes distrust a person without reason? Yes (B) No (A)	

score

9 Would you attend a seance?

Yes (B)   No (A)

10 Have you ever been to a place and felt that you have been there before?

Yes (B)   No (A)

11 Do you believe that dreams have meaning?

Yes (B)   No (A)

12 Do you read between the lines when you talk to people?

Yes (B)   No (A)

13 Have you ever known when a telephone was about to ring?

Yes (B)   No (A)

14 Have you ever guessed in advance what someone was about to tell you?

Yes (B)   No (A)

15 Do you believe that you can influence the roll of a die?

Yes (B)   No (A)

16 Do you sometimes say something at the exact moment someone else says it?

Yes (B)   No (A)

82

17 Do you believe that animals have greater intuition than humans?

Yes (B)   No (A)

18 Can you sense forthcoming danger?

Yes (B)   No (A)

19 Do you believe in love at first sight?

Yes (B)   No (A)

20 Do you ever sense hostility from people who appear to be friendly?

Yes (B)   No (A)

21 Do you believe in mind over matter?

Yes (B)   No (A)

22 Can you sometimes feel the emotions of someone who is not physically present?

Yes (B)   No (A)

23 Do you feel drawn to certain people even though you don't know them well?

Yes (B)   No (A)

24 Do you believe that twins have a special affinity?

Yes (B)   No (A)

score

25 Do you have a special affinity with animals?

Yes (B)   No (A)

26 Do you believe in the laws of probability?

No (B)   Yes (A)

27 Can you sometimes foretell the future?

Yes (B)   No (A)

28 Would you go to a fortune-teller?

Yes (B)   No (A)

29 Are you sometimes aware of unspoken undercurrents in social situations?

Yes (B)   No (A)

30 Do you often guess the end of a story before you have reached it?

Yes (B)   No (A)

31 Do you believe in reincarnation?

Yes (B)   No (A)

32 Do you believe that cats are more sensitive than human beings?

Yes (B)   No (A)

33 Do you believe that dogs can recognize their masters by their footsteps?

Yes (B)   No (A)

34 Can you sense when someone is behind you even though you cannot see or hear them?

Yes (B)   No (A)

35 Do your dreams ever come true?

Yes (B)   No (A)

36 Can you sometimes guess a person's occupation without any real clues?

Yes (B)   No (A)

37 Do odd coincidences regularly happen in your life?

Yes (B)   No (A)

38 Do you ever wish for something to happen?

Yes (B)   No (A)

39 Would you enjoy the work of a psychotherapist?

Yes (B)   No (A)

40 Do you sometimes feel that facts merely cloud an issue?

Yes (B)   No (A)

41 Would you trust your intuition even in a very important matter where a mistake would be serious?

Yes (B) No (A)

42 Do you know when it is going to rain?

Yes (B) No (A)

43 Do you sometimes think of friends at the same moment they think of you?

Yes (B) No (A)

44 Do you believe in natural medicines?

Yes (B) No (A)

45 Do you believe in divination by Tarot cards, I Ching, etc?

Yes (B) No (A)

46 Do you sometimes know the sender of a letter without looking?

Yes (B) No (A)

47 Do you believe in the supernatural?

Yes (B) No (A)

48 Can you sense when people disagree with you even if they may be trying to hide it?

Yes (B) No (A)

49 Do you rely on your intuition in many different circumstances?

Yes (B)   No (A)

50 Do you believe that animals can sense forthcoming earthquakes?

Yes (B)   No (A)

Scoring

A = 0 points
B = 2 points

82–100
Extremely powerful intuition.
62–80
Strong intuitive feeling.
42–60
Average intuitive ability.

22–40
Very down to earth.
0–20
No intuition apparent.

How did you do? If you scored very highly on the intuition scale, then you are the sort of person for whom the 'feel' of an individual or situation is of paramount importance. You pay great attention to the non-verbal signals that everyone gives out, even when these are received only at a subliminal level.

Most intuitive people talk about this faculty rather as though they possessed sensitive feelers, like those of certain insects, that can detect very slight changes in their environment. The down side of being highly intuitive is that you may be less observant of facts than other people. You may also find it hard to convince the people around you of the validity of your feelings when forced to concede that they are 'only' based on intuitive insights.

If you are a low scorer, then all this talk of intuition will just make you annoyed. You will feel that you are a practical person with no time for flights of fancy. Although you will be far more likely to give due regard to the facts of a situation, you may well miss out on subtleties and nuances that more intuitive people would easily notice.

Are you an extrovert?

The time has come to book the next summer holiday. Would you decide on:

		score
a.	A stay in a farm in the French countryside.	
b.	Hiring a villa in a Greek seaside resort with a group of friends.	
c.	An all-inclusive holiday in a Spanish holiday village with all-day sports and entertainment.	

You have a couple of hours to spare in the afternoon. Do you:

a.	Phone a friend who lives nearby and invite him/her over for a coffee.	
b.	Catch up on some household chores that you have neglected for ages.	
c.	Have a lie down on your bed with a novel.	

You are asked by your boss to take a new business contact out to lunch. Do you:

a.	Look forward to the meeting and the discussion over lunch.	
b.	Dread it and wish it was already over.	
c.	Regard it as part of the job but without much enthusiasm.	

A new couple move in next door. Do you: **score**

a.	Try to catch them on their way out and introduce yourself.	
b.	Knock on their door the first evening and invite them over for a glass of wine.	
c.	Wait until you bump into them to say hello.	

(item 4)

A friend invites you to her party where you will only know very few people. Do you:

a.	Look forward to the chance of meeting some new people.	
b.	Tell her you are busy that evening and invite her around on her own on a different evening instead.	
c.	Go to the party but mainly talk to the few people you already know.	

(item 5)

A friend suggests joining a social club in your village. Would you:

a.	Tell her you are far too busy as you hate joining any kind of club.	
b.	Join the club to keep her company but secretly wish you did not have to go.	
c.	Tell her what a wonderful idea it is and how much you would enjoy getting to know other people in the village.	

(item 6)

You are looking for a new job. Would you consider a position that involves:

a.	Going abroad frequently with a team of colleagues.	
b.	Working on your own on a project that has fascinated you for a long time.	
c.	Working in a small office in liaison with a few other colleagues.	

(item 7)

On your way to the postbox a neighbor is walking toward you on the opposite side of the road. Do you:

8

a.	Walk across the road and make a comment on the weather.	
b.	Stay on the same side of the road and give a weak smile.	
c.	Stop and have a 15-minute chat.	

After a forecast predicting rain for the weekend, the weather has turned out better than expected. Do you:

9

a.	Spend the day decorating the living room as planned.	
b.	Go out for a long walk instead and do a bit of decorating later in the day.	
c.	Postpone decorating and try to book a hotel at the seaside on the spur of the moment.	

On a Sunday morning you ideally:

10

a.	Have a long lie in.	
b.	Go to the gym for a workout.	
c.	Do jobs around the house.	

You are to attend a meeting where an important issue is at stake. Do you:

11

a.	Sit down and make a detailed list of the points you might raise.	
b.	Have a think one hour before the meeting about what you might say.	
c.	Go into the meeting unprepared and take part in the discussion as you go along.	

You move to a new area. Do you: **score**

12

a.	Join a local club and take up a new hobby.	
b.	Join an evening class to carry on with your studies in French.	
c.	Decide you are too busy to join anything but carry on seeing a few friends from your previous location.	

You are offered a high-paid job building up a company that has been in existence for only three months. Do you:

13

a.	Jump at the chance of the new challenge lying ahead of you.	
b.	Stick with the familiarity of the job you have had for the past few years – the new job's prospects sound far too risky to you.	
c.	Keep looking for a job with a more established company, though you would have loved the change.	

You go to a meeting at your children's school. Do you:

14

a.	Enthuse about the chance to discuss various issues with a group of parents.	
b.	Listen to what the other parents have to say but do not feel you could make a contribution yourself.	
c.	Throw in the occasional comment.	

You have decided to do some charity work. Do you choose to:

15

a.	Sort out clothes donations in a local charity shop.	
b.	Carry out door-to-door collections.	
c.	Arrange and hold fund-raising activities.	

Christmas is coming up in one month's time. You: **score**

16	a.	Bought and wrapped up all your presents four weeks earlier.	
	b.	Are looking through catalogues for gift ideas.	
	c.	Leave all the shopping until the weekend before Christmas.	

A friend tells you a person close to her is suffering from a terminal illness. Do you:

17	a.	Get terribly upset and think of nothing else all day.	
	b.	Listen with sympathy and comfort your friend.	
	c.	Listen politely but with detachment – after all, the dying woman is not a personal friend of yours.	

For the third time in a row your partner has come home late from work without phoning you, and again the dinner is ruined. Do you:

18	a.	Lose your temper, shout at her the moment she gets in and ask her to get herself a take-away if she wants to eat.	
	b.	Not show her you are angry but tell her rationally that it would really be better to phone.	
	c.	Show her you're annoyed and make it clear that this is the last meal you have wasted.	

You have been doing the same job for 10 years and feel fed up. Do you:

19	a.	Hand in your notice on the spur of the moment because you cannot stand it any longer.	
	b.	Buy the local paper and browse through the job ads.	
	c.	Persevere with the job as it is well paid and familiar to you.	

A relative unexpectedly cancels an invitation for Saturday night. Do you:

20

a.	Invite a few close friends to a dinner party.	
b.	Go to a lively dance at your local community centre.	
c.	Hire a video.	

You are trying to find an address but seem to have lost your way. You haven't got a map. Do you:

21

a.	Walk back to the point you set out from and start again.	
b.	Ask the next person you come across for directions.	
c.	Buy a chocolate bar in a newsagents further down the road and ask the shop assistant for the way.	

You have decided to start exercising. Do you:

22

a.	Join a local sports team.	
b.	Go jogging before breakfast.	
c.	Play tennis with a friend.	

You are planning a day out. Do you choose to:

23

a.	Go to an amusement park and go on lots of white-knuckle rides.	
b.	Spend a relaxing day on the beach.	
c.	Go to a leisure pool with slides and other water features.	

A morning of household chores lies ahead of you. Do you: **score**

24

a.	Get them done as quickly as possible so that you can get on with other things.	
b.	Do them at a leisurely pace with a cup of coffee halfway through.	
c.	Do them thoroughly but without stopping in between.	

A public figure you admired has been killed. Do you:

25

a.	Wonder what all the fuss is about – after all he was not personally known to you.	
b.	Watch his funeral on television crying your eyes out.	
c.	Attend the public funeral and join other mourners in their grief.	

After Sunday lunch you have an hour to spare. Do you choose to:

26

a.	Take a nap.	
b.	Do some work in the garden.	
c.	Phone friends for a chat.	

You decide to spend the evening watching television. Would you watch:

27

a.	A concert.	
b.	A current affairs documentary.	
c.	A game show.	

You are taking part in a planning meeting on a new project for the future. Are you:
score

a.	Full of ideas about the overall nature of the project.	
b.	Keen on devising ways of carrying out the project.	
c.	Able to throw in suggestions on both aspects.	

You are offered the chance of a trip abroad the following weekend. Do you:

a.	Accept it immediately without hesitation.	
b.	Say you would love to go but you need to check first about any previous engagements with your partner.	
c.	Weigh up carefully the pros and cons of the trip before making up your mind.	

You are enquiring about a holiday property. Do you:

a.	Phone the owners and ask them to send you a brochure.	
b.	Write to the owners for some information.	
c.	Phone the owners for information and discuss your requirements with them.	

You are on your way to do your weekly shopping. Do you:

a.	Go with a shopping list but allow yourself to be tempted to buy other items.	
b.	Only buy items that are on your shopping list as you could otherwise not keep any control over your spending.	
c.	Decide what to buy when you are in the store and worry about the shopping bill later.	

You are shopping in town and see an expensive dress that you would love to have. Do you:

score

a.	Buy it on the spur of the moment.	
b.	Decide to think it over when you get home and possibly buy it the next time you are in town.	
c.	Think about it while finishing the rest of the shopping and then go back for it.	

32

It's Friday and you have not made any arrangements for Saturday yet. Do you:

a.	Watch the weather forecast and plan out exactly what you want to do with your time off.	
b.	Decide on the day when you know what sort of mood you are in.	
c.	Have some ideas but do not make any firm plans.	

33

You are in a train reading a newspaper when another passenger sits down in your compartment. Do you:

a.	Ignore the person and carry on reading your paper.	
b.	Look up briefly, say hello and then bury your head in the paper again.	
c.	Try starting a conversation.	

34

An acquaintance asks you to carry out a door-to-door collection for a good cause. Do you:

a.	Agree to do it with enthusiasm as it seems a good way of raising money.	
b.	Decline politely as you hate knocking on strangers' doors asking for money.	
c.	Agree to it as you find it difficult to say no.	

35

You have to make a speech on a social occasion. Do you: **score**

36

a.	Write it out beforehand and learn it by heart.	
b.	Make a few notes on the points you want to address.	
c.	Improvise when the occasion arises.	

You are asked to sign a credit agreement. Do you:

37

a.	Decide to take it home and read it through quietly before signing anything.	
b.	Sign immediately as the sales consultant has explained everything you feel you need to know.	
c.	Read the agreement through carefully, including the small print, and then sign it in the store.	

You meet somebody you know by sight on a bus and he starts a conversation with you. Do you:

38

a.	Feel uncomfortable because you do not know what to talk about.	
b.	Make a few polite comments so as not to appear unsociable.	
c.	Feel happy to have met somebody to pass the time with on the bus journey.	

You are thinking of booking a weekend break. Would you consider:

39

a.	A horse-riding weekend with a group of strangers.	
b.	A multi-sports weekend with a close friend.	
c.	A stay in a seaside cottage with your partner.	

You are attending a large office party. Do you: **score**

40	a.	Talk to a wide variety of people and tend to dominate the conversation.	
	b.	Talk predominantly to the people you work with and know well.	
	c.	Tend to stay in the background and only make the odd remark.	

You are invited to a talk about possible life in space followed by a discussion session. Do you:

41	a.	Accept the invitation with anticipation.	
	b.	Go to the talk as you have not got anything better to do.	
	c.	Decline the invitation and go to your local bar instead.	

You are in the company of a few friends. Do you prefer to:

42	a.	Have a serious discussion on a subject of interest.	
	b.	Crack some jokes and have a good laugh.	
	c.	Talk about some everyday matters.	

You are working on a project. Do you:

43	a.	Pay attention to all the details and double-check everything you write.	
	b.	Concentrate on the broad issues of the project, as the details are unimportant.	
	c.	Write steadily and read it through to eliminate any obvious mistakes once you have finished.	

Christmas is on your doorstep. Do you look forward to: **score**

44

a.	A quiet few days spent with your family.	
b.	The opportunity to see a few close friends during the period.	
c.	The chance to go to some lively Christmas parties.	

The weather is awful and you are faced with a Sunday morning reading the paper. Do you:

45

a.	Feel delighted that for once you have a chance for a good read.	
b.	Hate the idea of sitting around all morning.	
c.	Read the paper for a while but then occupy yourself with a few jobs.	

Your partner tells you it's time to invite some friends and colleagues to a party at your home. Are you:

46

a.	Full of enthusiasm and look forward to organizing the event.	
b.	Nervous at the prospect, but feel it is your duty to do it.	
c.	Keen to convince your partner that it can really wait for a bit longer.	

A couple of friends phone up and ask if they could stay with you for a week. Do you:

47

a.	Tell them you just haven't got enough space, as you cannot bear the thought of having somebody staying for that long.	
b.	Invite them to stay as you do not want to hurt their feelings.	
c.	Look forward to having constant company for a week.	

You are told by your boss that you will have to do a lot of foreign travelling within the next few months. Do you:

48

a.	Love the idea of seeing new places and meeting new people.	
b.	Quite like the idea but do not enjoy being away from your family.	
c.	Dread the prospect of changing your routine.	

You are offered a summer job organizing entertainment in a holiday village. Do you:

49

a.	Grasp the opportunity as the job should be fun and you are bound to meet lots of people.	
b.	Take the job as nothing better has come up.	
c.	Decline the offer as you would hate a job where you are constantly surrounded by people.	

A friend asks you to accompany her to a pottery class for the first time. Do you:

50

a.	Go with her just to be helpful.	
b.	Tell her you do not want to go as you have never done pottery before.	
c.	Love the idea of trying out something new.	

Scoring

For each answer score the number of points indicated.

1. a:1, b:2, c:3	**14.** a:3, b:1, c:2	**27.** a:1, b:2, c:3	**40.** a:3, b:2, c:1
2. a:3, b:2, c:1	**15.** a:1, b:2, c:3	**28.** a:3, b:2, c:1	**41.** a:3, b:2, c:1
3. a:3, b:1, c:2	**16.** a:1, b:2, c:3	**29.** a:3, b:2, c:1	**42.** a:1, b:3, c:2
4. a:2, b:3, c:1	**17.** a:3, b:2, c:1	**30.** a:2, b:1, c:3	**43.** a:1, b:3, c:2
5. a:3, b:1, c:2	**18.** a:3, b:1, c:2	**31.** a:2, b:1, c:3	**44.** a:1, b:2, c:3
6. a:1, b:2, c:3	**19.** a:3, b:2, c:1	**32.** a:3, b:1, c:2	**45.** a:1, b:3, c2
7. a:3, b:1, c:2	**20.** a:2, b:3, c:1	**33.** a:1, b:3, c:2	**46.** a:3, b:2, c:1
8. a:1, b:2, c:3	**21.** a:1, b:3, c:2	**34.** a:1, b:2, c:3	**47.** a:1, b:2, c:3
9. a:2, b:1, c:3	**22.** a:3, b:1, c:2	**35.** a:3, b:1, c:2	**48.** a:3, b:2, c:1
10. a:1, b:3, c:2	**23.** a:3, b:1, c:2	**36.** a:1, b:2, c:3	**49.** a:3, b:2, c:1
11. a:1, b:2, c:3	**24.** a:3, b:1, c:2	**37.** a:1, b:3, c:2	**50.** a:2, b:1, c:3
12. a:3, b:2, c:1	**25.** a:1, b:2, c:3	**38.** a:1, b:2, c:3	
13. a:3, b:1, c:2	**26.** a:1, b:2, c:3	**39.** a:3, b:2, c:1	

Over 125

The maximum score is 150. Anything over 125 would suggest that you are extremely extrovert. Your main love is communicating with other people and you feel lonely and uncomfortable when confronted with solitary tasks. You are also socially bold and enjoy taking risks. Your idea of hell is an evening spent alone with a book.

100–124

If you scored between 100 and 124, you are still quite extrovert but are not so dependent on other people that you suffer withdrawal symptoms when left alone.

75–99

If your score was between 75 and 99, you are average. You enjoy company but can easily spend time alone and enjoy that too. You are by no means cautious but you feel no compulsion to take risks or to involve yourself in situations where the spotlight is upon you.

60–74

If you scored between 60 and 74, you are quite introverted and on the whole prefer to keep away from social situations. You find that you are most at ease when allowed to get on with solitary tasks.

Below 60

If you scored below 60, you are really very introverted and find the society of others stressful. You will happily work alone and, if allowed to do so, will also spend your leisure hours in quiet pursuits.

Test Six

Are you driven?

Some psychologists are fond of referring to something called 'Type A behavior.' What they mean is the sort of hard-driving, impatient, irascible behaviour often displayed by people in positions of authority. Although it is not inevitable that a Type A person should be the boss, it is quite likely because such people push themselves, and are thus often highly successful. However, there is a penalty to be paid for this Type A behavior: it goes hand in hand with high levels of stress. This particular trait has been labeled 'the heart attack profile' because it was thought that those who exhibited such behavior were at increased risk of coronary illness (more recently, it has been suggested that heart disease is a risk only if the subject also exhibits high levels of animosity.) Try the following questions to discover just how you rate on the Type A scale.

1 Do you tend to drive too fast?

a. Often.   **b.** Never.   **c.** Sometimes.

2 Do you get impatient with other drivers?

a. Occasionally.   **b.** Regularly.   **c.** Never.

3 Would you try to push ahead of others?

a. No.   **b.** Yes.   **c.** Unsure.

4 Are you willing to wait patiently for what you want?

a. Yes.   **b.** Unsure.   **c.** No.

5 Do you set high standards of achievement for yourself?

a. Sometimes.   **b.** Always.   **c.** Never.

6 Do you suffer fools gladly?

a. Never.   **b.** Sometimes.   **c.** Usually.

7 Do you lose your temper when frustrated?

a. Not really.   **b.** Yes.   **c.** Sometimes.

8 Do you bang doors shut?

a. Often.   **b.** Sometimes.   **c.** Never.

9 Can you relax easily after a day's work?

a. Yes.   **b.** No.   **c.** Usually.

10 Do you take your work troubles home with you?

a. Often.   **b.** Occasionally.   **c.** Seldom.

11 Are you quite happy to let others go in front of you?

a. No.   **b.** Yes.   **c.** Maybe.

12 Do you yell at other drivers because you get impatient?

a. Occasionally.   **b.** Never.   **c.** Often.

13 Do you get to work early and leave late?

a. No.   **b.** Yes.   **c.** Occasionally.

14 Do you feel there are not enough hours in the day to get everything done?

a. Occasionally.   **b.** Often.   **c.** Seldom.

15 Do you take all your annual holiday?

a. Always.   **b.** Sometimes.   **c.** Never.

16 Do you aspire to a senior management job?

a. Yes.   **b.** No.   **c.** Unsure.

17 Are you impatient to succeed?

a. Sometimes.   **b.** Yes.   **c.** No.

18 Do you enjoy spending time with your friends and family?

a. Usually.   **b.** Always.   **c.** Seldom.

19 Do you have lots of hobbies?

a. Yes.   **b.** No.   **c.** A few.

20 Do you (or did you) play sports that require aggression?

a. Often.   **b.** Sometimes.   **c.** Never.

21 Would you spend Sunday morning just reading the newspapers?

a. No.   **b.** Yes.   **c.** Maybe.

22 Do you suffer from high blood pressure?

a. Don't know.   **b.** Yes.   **c.** No.

23 Do you get impatient at other people's mistakes?

a. Frequently.   **b.** Never.   **c.** Sometimes.

24 Are you glad when it's time to go home after a day's work?

a. Yes.   **b.** No.   **c.** Not especially.

25 Has your doctor ever told you to take it easy?

a. Often.   **b.** Sometimes.   **c.** Never.

Scoring

For each answer score the number of points indicated.

1. a:3, b:1, c:2	**8.** a:3, b:2, c:1	**15.** a:1, b:2, c:3	**22.** a:2, b:3, c:1
2. a:2, b:3, c:1	**9.** a:1, b:3, c:2	**16.** a:3, b:1, c:2	**23.** a:3, b:1, c:2
3. a:1, b:3, c:2	**10.** a:3, b:2, c:1	**17.** a:2, b:3, c:1	**24.** a:1, b:3, c:2
4. a:1, b:2, c:3	**11.** a:3, b:1, c:2	**18.** a:2, b:1, c:3	**25.** a:3, b:2, c:1
5. a:2, b:3, c:1	**12.** a:2, b:1, c:3	**19.** a:1, b:3, c:2	
6. a:3, b:2, c:1	**13.** a:1, b:3, c:2	**20.** a:3, b:2, c:1	
7. a:1, b:3, c:2	**14.** a:2, b:3, c:1	**21.** a:3, b:1, c:2	

Over 65

Maximum score is 75. If you scored 65 or above, you are a typical Type A: impatient and rather aggressive. You probably have a successful career, but your home life may well suffer as a result. Your impatience may put you at some risk from car accidents, and your tendency to be aggressive might provoke a similar response from others.

55–64

If you scored 55 to 64, you are almost a Type A personality and probably find relaxation the hardest thing to do. You tend to overwork and find it difficult to unwind at the end of the day. Your health could suffer because of the constant stress you live with. You would be well advised to learn how to take things a bit easier.

45–54

If you scored from 45 to 54, you are quite balanced. You have enough get up and go to get things done, but you are not so over-stressed that it is likely to affect your health. You know how to push for what you want but can back off when it is advisable to do so.

30–44

If you scored from 30 to 44, you are really quite relaxed and find all this Type A stuff a little perplexing. After all, what's the hurry?

Below 30

If you scored below 30, you are a very relaxed type who is quite happy to let others do the rushing. Ambition does not bother you much; you take time to enjoy life.

Are you a schemer?

Niccolò Machiavelli was an Italian political writer at the time of the
Renaissance. His book *The Prince* became notorious for its rather
amoral outlook, and his name has therefore entered the language to
describe people who plot, plan, calculate, double-cross and trust no
one but themselves. People who score highly on such a scale usually
think of themselves as hard-boiled and realistic. They feel that
most other people are just too naive to live. Machiavellianism may
not be the most attractive personality trait, but it is widely found
among people who wheel and deal for a living. A naive and trusting
politician, for example, would not last long. A Machiavellian one
might end up as head honcho. See how you measure up on this
scale.

		score
1	Do you always assume that people have some sort of ulterior motive?	
	a. Yes. **b.** No. **c.** Unsure.	
2	Do you check up on people to find out whether they've told you the truth?	
	a. Never. **b.** Sometimes. **c.** Always.	
3	Would you agree that virtue is really just insufficient temptation?	
	a. Unsure. **b.** Yes. **c.** No.	
4	Do you think that most people have their price?	
	a. No. **b.** Unsure. **c.** Yes.	
5	Would you make a good politician?	
	a. Unsure. **b.** Yes. **c.** No.	
6	Do you believe what you see in advertisements?	
	a. Never. **b.** Sometimes. **c.** Often.	
7	Do you regard statistics as a way of covering up lies?	
	a. Occasionally. **b.** Often. **c.** Seldom.	
8	Are there many people you would trust completely?	
	a. Plenty. **b.** Almost none. **c.** Quite few.	

9 If someone was collecting for charity, would you trust them to use the money properly?

a. Maybe. **b.** No. **c.** Yes.

10 If someone is accused of a crime are you inclined to believe them guilty?

a. No. **b.** Yes. **c.** Sometimes.

11 Do you regard your work colleagues as friends or competitors?

a. Competitors. **b.** Friends. **c.** In between.

12 Would you trust the word of a priest?

a. Possibly. **b.** Probably. **c.** No.

13 Would you lie to get what you want?

a. Yes. **b.** Unsure. **c.** No.

14 Do you believe that the end justifies the means?

a. Unsure. **b.** Yes. **c.** No.

15 Would you trust the word of a politician?

a. Never. **b.** Seldom. **c.** Frequently.

16 Do you see relations between the sexes as a battlefield?

a. Sometimes. **b.** Always. **c.** Never.

17 If you read a newspaper article do you look for flaws and inaccuracies?

a. Always.   b. Never.   c. Sometimes.

18 Will people take advantage of you if you let them?

a. Never.   b. Seldom.   c. Often.

19 Is it better to trick someone before they do it to you?

a. Yes.   b. No.   c. Unsure.

20 Would you pull off a smart business deal even though it was not quite honest?

a. No.   b. Yes.   c. Maybe.

21 Do you believe that most people would help you if you were in trouble?

a. No.   b. Maybe.   c. Yes.

22 Could you sell second-hand cars?

a. Maybe.   b. Yes.   c. No.

23 Do you sometimes give people information calculated to mislead them?

a. Yes.   b. No.   c. Maybe.

24 Do you pride yourself on your ability to outwit others?

a. Sometimes.   b. Never.   c. Frequently.

25 Would you rather be thought of as smart or honest?

a. Smart.   b. Unsure.   c. Honest.

SCORING

For each answer score the number of points indicated.

1.	a:3, b:1, c:2	**8.**	a:1, b:3, c:2	**15.**	a:3, b:2, c:1	**22.**	a:2, b:3, c:1
2.	a:1, b:2, c:3	**9.**	a:2, b:3, c:1	**16.**	a:2, b:3, c:1	**23.**	a:3, b:1, c:2
3.	a:2, b:3, c:1	**10.**	a:1, b:3, c:2	**17.**	a:3, b:1, c:2	**24.**	a:2, b:1, c:3
4.	a:1, b:2, c:3	**11.**	a:3, b:1, c:2	**18.**	a:1, b:2, c:3	**25.**	a:3, b:2, c:1
5.	a:2, b:3, c:1	**12.**	a:2, b:1, c:3	**19.**	a:3, b:1, c:2		
6.	a:3, b:2, c:1	**13.**	a:3, b:2, c:1	**20.**	a:1, b:3, c:2		
7.	a:2, b:3, c:1	**14.**	a:2, b:3, c:1	**21.**	a:3, b:2, c:1		

Over 65

Maximum score is 75. If you scored 65 or above you are a pretty tough nut. You don't trust other people, are prepared to lie and trick your way to get what you want, and have few scruples about the methods you employ. You will either be very successful or serve time in prison. Possibly both.

55–64

If you scored 55 to 64 Machiavelli would still have cause to be proud of you. He would admire your capacity for assessing others shrewdly and not being swayed by any silly sentimentality about people's motives.

45–54

If you scored 45 to 54 you are quite tricky enough to survive in a hard world, but you do have some scruples and are not really as unscrupulous as you might think.

35–44

A score of 35 to 44 indicates that you're really something of a softie. You actually believe that others can have good motives and you are unwilling to use any means to get what you want.

30–34

A score of 30 to 34 suggests that you are a really nice person but will regularly get taken advantage of by people who do not share your sunny view of human nature.

Below 30

If you scored below 30, you are probably not safe to go out alone.

Test Eight

Are you ambitious?

For some people material success is the motivating force of their entire lives. They are engaged in a constant struggle to get to the top, and find this mission more important than other considerations, such as home, family and leisure pursuits. Others are quite unconcerned with climbing the greasy pole and are happy to live a more modest life in less stressful circumstances. Which are you? The following test should help show you.

		score

1 Did you know what career you wanted even when you were still at school?

a. Yes.　　　　b. No.　　　　c. Not sure.

2 Do you agree that 'the best things in life are free'?

a. Yes.　　　　b. Unsure.　　　　c. No.

3 Is winning important to you?

a. Unsure.　　　　b. Yes.　　　　c. No.

4 Do you work more than you have to?

a. No.　　　　b. Unsure.　　　　c. Yes.

5 Do you feel you need a high salary?

a. Yes.　　　　b. Perhaps.　　　　c. No.

6 Have you got your next promotion planned?

a. No.　　　　b. Yes.　　　　c. Unsure.

7 Would you make a good ship's captain?

a. Unsure.　　　　b. No.　　　　c. Yes.

8 Would you accept a lower salary if you could spend more time with your family?

a. Yes.　　　　b. No.　　　　c. Unsure.

			score

9 Would you compete with a friend for promotion even though it might endanger your relationship?

a. Yes.   b. Unsure.   c. No.

10 Do you long to emulate successful people?

a. No.   b. Unsure.   c. Yes.

11 Do you feel discontented with your current level of prosperity?

a. Unsure.   b. No.   c. Yes.

12 Do you have a plan for the development of your career?

a. Yes.   b. Unsure.   c. No.

13 Would you take a day off on the spur of the moment?

a. Yes.   b. Unsure.   c. No.

14 Do you admire people who are ruthless in pursuit of success?

a. Yes.   b. No. c. Unsure.

15 Would you agree that 'the love of money is the root of all evil?'

a. Unsure.   b. Yes.   c. No.

16 Do you enjoy the luxuries that money can buy?

a. No. **b.** Yes. **c.** Unsure.

17 Who do you admire more, Madonna or Mahatma Gandhi?

a. Madonna. **b.** Gandhi. **c.** Unsure.

18 Do you like to spend time messing about in the garden?

a. Yes. **b.** No. **c.** Unsure.

19 Do you think about your work much during your free time?

a. Sometimes. **b.** Often. **c.** Seldom.

20 Is status of much concern to you?

a. No. **b.** Yes. **c.** Unsure.

21 Is it important to you to drive a new, powerful car?

a. Unsure. **b.** No. **c.** Yes.

22 Would you expect to succeed in politics?

a. Yes. **b.** Unsure. **c.** No.

23 Do you dream of giving up the rat race and doing something less stressful?

a. Yes. **b.** Unsure. **c.** No.

24 Do people regard you mainly with affection or mainly with respect?

a. Respect. **b.** Affection. **c.** Unsure.

25 Do you ever socialize with people just because they are useful to you?

a. No. **b.** Unsure. **c.** Yes.

SCORING

For each answer score the number of points indicated.

1. a:3, b:1, c:2	**8.** a:1, b:3, c:2	**15.** a:2, b:1, c:3	**22.** a:3, b:2, c:1
2. a:1, b:2, c:3	**9.** a:3, b:2, c:1	**16.** a:1, b:3, c:2	**23.** a:1, b:2, c:3
3. a:2, b:3, c:1	**10.** a:1, b:2, c:3	**17.** a:3, b:1, c:2	**24.** a:3, b:1, c:2
4. a:1, b:2, c:3	**11.** a:2, b:1, c:3	**18.** a:1, b:3, c:2	**25.** a:1, b:2, c:3
5. a:3, b:2, c:1	**12.** a:3, b:2, c:1	**19.** a:2, b:3, c:1	
6. a:1, b:3, c:2	**13.** a:1, b:2, c:3	**20.** a:1, b:3, c:2	
7. a:2, b:1, c:3	**14.** a:3, b:1, c:2	**21.** a:2, b:1, c:3	

Over 65

Maximum score is 75. If you scored 65 or above, ambition is clearly of the greatest importance to you. You are the sort of person who will succeed or die! You may find that other areas of your life are fairly empty, but though you may have cause for some regret, you will always feel that you have carried out your mission to succeed.

55–64

In this range, you are still quite ambitious and will spend most of your time trying to make your career a success. In spite of your success, you might have regrets about things you have left undone.

45–54

In this range, you are quite keen on your career but by no means obsessed with it. You want to do well, but think that there is more to life than getting ahead.

35–44

In this range, ambition does not mean that much to you. You enjoy other aspects of your life just as much, and are willing to accept a lower standard of living if you can be happy.

30–34

In this range, you are really not ambitious at all. You value your free time and have many things you would rather do than struggle for material gain. You are not very status-conscious and cannot understand what makes people struggle so hard to succeed.

Below 30

If you scored below 30 you probably have no idea what ambition means.

Test **Nine**

Are you honest?

Honesty is one of those virtues that everyone insists on, claims
resolutely for themselves and criticizes their rivals for not possessing.
Yet if we are really honest, we must admit that there are always grey
areas – that we all, from time to time, bend the rules a little, and that
anyone who was totally, utterly and embarrassingly honest would be a
massive pain. Try the following test to see just how you measure up in
the honesty stakes.

You oversleep for a crucial business meeting at work. When you dash in, breathless and flustered, do you apologize by:

score

a.	Declaring your dog had been hit by a speeding car and demanded urgent veterinary attention.	
b.	Cursing alarm clocks and admitting your dismal failure to wake up.	
c.	Blaming the dreadful traffic for holding you up.	

For the fourth consecutive year, you forget your sensitive best friend's birthday. On the special day do you:

a.	Ring up and apologize profusely, sending a huge box of chocolates round by courier to try and make amends.	
b.	Totally bluff it, calling to give birthday wishes, and asking if they liked the non-existent card and thoughtful present you sent three days ago.	
c.	Rush out to buy a card, stick it in the post, and later admit that you only remembered yesterday, but the card should have arrived by now.	

You are just about to draw some money out at a cash point when you realize the previous customer's cash card is still firmly held and registered in the machine. Do you:

a.	Curiously check out the balance but refuse to give in to temptation, ejecting the card and handing it in to the bank.	
b.	Hastily withdraw the card, calling out and looking around to see if the rightful owner is nearby.	
c.	Cast a quick glance around to check no one is near before drawing out some easy cash, later dropping the card anonymously into the bank.	

On entering your kitchen one morning, you find your housemates in the midst of a blistering debate over who left the freezer door open last night and succeeded in defrosting its entire contents. It was you. Do you:

score

a.	Grab a bowl of cereal, claiming you're late for work and don't have time to discuss it right now.	
b.	Vehemently deny you had anything to do with it, elaborating on how you ate out last night anyway.	
c.	Offer your abject apologies for your mistake, offering to compensate the others for their losses.	

While out on a shopping trip you notice a bulging wallet on the floor at your feet. Do you:

a.	Pick it up surreptitiously, extracting a wad of cash and a tempting credit card, and casually drop it back on the ground.	
b.	Take it to the nearest police station without even glancing at its contents.	
c.	Check out the details of the owner, later ringing him and enquiring if there's a reward for its safe return.	

Your sister parades around, showing off her latest designer outfit. Alas the skirt is unflatteringly short, the top is too tight and the color clashes horribly with her hair. When asked for your opinion do you:

a.	Mutter an inoffensive, 'That's nice. Did I tell you that dress you were wearing yesterday looked fantastic?'	
b.	Announce that it doesn't do much to flatter her, refusing the urge to ask if she's wearing it for a bet.	
c.	A few splutters later, comment, 'It's different,' before making a hasty exit.	

Your partner has spent the day agonizingly cooking up a feast for a special treat. Unfortunately, you loathe the main ingredient, and the meal tastes revolting. When asked if you like it, do you:

7

			score
a.	Explain apologetically that you're allergic to pickled turnips, and ask if they would mind terribly if you snacked on something else.		
b.	Gulp it down to get rid of it as quickly as possible, nodding expressively to show how delicious it is.		
c.	Play with the food, and declare your boss took you out for a huge lunch you couldn't refuse so you can't appreciate this properly when you're still so full.		

Builders have been wandering in and out of your house during a course of renovation. You've made a point of covering the hall carpet to prevent any damage, but in fact it needs replacing and is insured against such things as damage due to building work. When the idea of putting in a claim to fund a replacement springs up, do you:

8

a.	Become more lax about protecting the carpet so that when damage actually does occur, your claim is justified.	
b.	Dismiss the idea as fraudulent and start saving for a new one yourself.	
c.	Rip the carpet up, leaving it outside to deteriorate with the other building waste and put in that claim – you're entitled to something back for all your premiums.	

A wild night partying ends in disaster as you accidentally leave a match burning on a table, which later leads to a minor but still damaging fire at your host's home. When the cause of the blaze is being discussed, do you:

score

9

a.	Keep quiet, safe in the knowledge that your friend is insured and no one was hurt.	
b.	Loudly slate those careless individuals who are a danger to our homes and safety.	
c.	Call your host the following day to admit your negligence and apologize.	

A colleague presents you with her long-awaited manuscript for a novel. Eager for your opinion, she calls you a week later to seek your approval. Alas the storyline is predictable and the dialogue is poorly written. Do you:

10

a.	Tell her you were really enthralled, and she should send it out to prospective publishers.	
b.	Comment on how much work must have gone into it, but gingerly suggest a few improvements and say that it might need editing a bit.	
c.	Declare that you're more into science fiction and are not really the right person to ask for an opinion.	

The day of an important corporate exam is drawing near, and your confidence isn't at its best. While waiting for your supervisor to return to her office, you notice the confidential exam documents lurking on her desk. Do you:

score

11

a.	Refuse to let yourself be tempted – you'd only be fooling yourself.	
b.	Whip the documents into your bag, photocopy them and return them when no one's around.	
c.	Have a quick peek to get the general idea but hastily put them back to appease your guilt.	

A department store's security bells start screaming out as you leave the shop. Is this most likely to be because:

12

a.	The system's faulty and is frequently set off for no reason.	
b.	You accidentally forgot to pay for your book, and went to walk out with it still in your hand.	
c.	You were short of cash and couldn't resist slipping the novel into your bag – a big department store won't suffer from that after all.	

Leaving a parking space goes disastrously wrong and you reverse back into an immaculate sports car parked behind you. To your relief nobody has witnessed your bad judgement, which has left the sports car's bumper badly, and expensively, dented. Do you: **score**

a.	Leave a note that says, 'The people watching all think I'm leaving you my name and address, but of course I'm doing no such thing!'	
b.	Attach a note to the sports car's windscreen with an apology and details of how to get in touch to sort out compensation.	
c.	Hang around for a while to see if the owner returns, but drive off after a while when you're convinced the damage is largely superficial.	

Your monthly pay has accidentally been paid into your bank account twice. Do you:

a.	Contact the bank and your employer immediately to rectify the mistake.	
b.	Rush out and spend, spend, spend before anyone can claim your windfall back.	
c.	Keep quiet about the error but make sure the money is still there in case anyone notices and claims it back.	

Having saved up for months, you finally splash out on the hi-fi of your dreams. At the cash desk, a daydreaming sales assistant undercharges you by a substantial amount. Do you:

a.	Pay up quickly and leave, thrilled with your good fortune.	
b.	Repeat the amount questioningly, but when the sales assistant still doesn't realize his mistake, pay the requested amount without quibbling.	
c.	Enlighten the sales assistant as to the true price of the equipment and pay up, pleased with your morals.	

Saturday night arrives, and you dress up to try and gain entry to an elite party you're not officially invited to attend. You nervously arrive at the party's entrance and psych yourself up to bluff an entry, when a prestigious guest greets you with a flourish and mistakenly assumes you to be another genuine invitee.
Do you:

16	a.	Humor your companion and assume the foreign guise for an evening of social indulgence.	
	b.	Exclaim that she must be mistaking you for someone else, but engage her in conversation so as to gain entrance.	
	c.	Go along with your new identity for a brief spell, then hastily lose your newfound friend and become a born-again you.	

A colleague dashes up to you one morning at work, breathless with thanks for your solving an unforeseen crisis yesterday. The problem is that wires have got crossed and you didn't have anything to do with it, but you know the person that did. Do you:

17	a.	Lap up the praise and promise to take him up on the favor he supposedly owes you.	
	b.	Change the subject without claiming responsibility – it might come in handy one day if the real benefactor doesn't make herself known.	
	c.	Confess it wasn't you and put in a good word for the colleague who really did the good deed.	

You agree to take on some urgent freelance work to supplement your salary. The work isn't done under supervision, and your temporary employer agrees to pay you on an hourly basis. When it comes to declaring the hours worked, do you:

score

18

a.	State the exact time spent working, to the nearest quarter of an hour.	
b.	Generously round up the hours to a reasonable length of time – anyone else would have taken longer.	
c.	Slightly over-estimate your working time, aware that the work is urgent and so is worth a bit of a premium.	

At the end of a glamorous ball, you discover your coveted coat is missing from the cloakroom. Do you:

19

a.	Grab a similar coat and hand it in to one of the organizers, hoping that its owner took your coat by mistake, and that if your own coat remains missing, you can claim the similar one as yours.	
b.	Peruse the array of coats, and randomly select a better model than your own to compensate you for your loss.	
c.	Explain your misfortune to the organizers, and keep calling to see if your coat has turned up – no need for anyone else to lose out.	

Would you consider lying to your mother as:

20

a.	Acceptable as long as it was just a little white lie and the truth would do more harm than good.	
b.	Completely natural – you rarely tell your mother the truth, as it usually ends in hassle.	
c.	Unthinkable – your relationship is totally open and she always knows if you're lying anyway.	

Do you consider lying to your boss as:

21

a.	An uncomfortable but sometimes necessary way of avoiding unemployment.	
b.	As unthinkable as lying to your mother – you try and avoid being in potentially lie-inspiring situations.	
c.	Fine – you have no problems manipulating the truth to your own advantage, even if it incriminates someone else.	

Which of the following is most likely to indicate when you last told a lie, of whatever magnitude?

22

a.	You can't remember – you rarely lie.	
b.	Yesterday, but it was in the form of an insincere compliment.	
c.	An hour ago – you just had to get rid of that annoying colleague somehow.	

An application form for your dream job demands details of experiences and skills you don't possess. Do you:

23

a.	Make it up from scratch, no problem.	
b.	Glorify your own experiences to match their criteria.	
c.	Chuck the form in the bin – you're obviously not suited to the job.	

Your partner finds an affectionate note from a friend unknown to him/her in your jacket pocket. Upon confrontation do you:

score

24

a.	Explain the simple, innocent truth – you'd never dream of having an affair.	
b.	Concoct an elaborate story to hide the truth of your illicit behavior.	
c.	Break down in tears, begging for forgiveness for your infidelity.	

To your horror, you accidentally knock a glass off a shelf, which careers down onto your computer, and crashes the system irretrievably. The computer is only guaranteed against technical faults, and not accidents. Do you:

25

a.	Put it down to bad luck, and start saving for a replacement.	
b.	Contact the computer company, claiming the machine just crashed and hoping some compensation will follow.	
c.	Enlist the help of an expert (if your own skills elude you) to adjust the system so that a technical fault looks likely, and you can claim a new model.	

Scoring

For each answer score the number of points indicated.

1.	a: 1, b: 3, c: 2	**10.**	a: 1, b: 3, c: 2	**19.**	a: 2, b: 1, c: 3
2.	a: 3, b: 1, c: 2	**11.**	a: 3, b: 1, c: 2	**20.**	a: 2, b: 1, c: 3
3.	a: 2, b: 3, c: 1	**12.**	a: 3, b: 2, c: 1	**21.**	a: 2, b: 3, c: 1
4.	a: 2, b: 1, c: 3	**13.**	a: 1, b: 3, c: 2	**22.**	a: 3, b: 2, c: 1
5.	a: 1, b: 3, c: 2	**14.**	a: 3, b: 1, c: 2	**23.**	a: 1, b: 2, c: 3
6.	a: 1, b: 3, c: 2	**15.**	a: 1, b: 2, c: 3	**24.**	a: 3, b: 1, c: 2
7.	a: 3, b: 1, c: 2	**16.**	a: 1, b: 3, c: 2	**25.**	a: 3, b: 2, c: 1
8.	a: 2, b: 3, c: 1	**17.**	a: 1, b: 2, c: 3		
9.	a: 2, b: 1, c: 3	**18.**	a: 3, b: 1, c: 2		

Maximum score is 75. With a score over 65, your position as a scrupulously honest member of society is irrefutable. Between 45 and 65 suggests you may twist the truth if no-one gets too hurt in the process. Nearing 30 means your scruples are very much out of shape. Below that, and woe betide anyone who trusts your word on anything; your addiction to lying is such that hearing an honest word pass your lips is almost as rare as spotting Halley's Comet.

Test Ten

Are you tenacious?

What do you do when the going gets tough? Do you roll up your
sleeves and get the job done, come hell or high water, or do you
wander off for a cup of coffee and let the others take care of it? In other
words, just how tenacious are you? Try the following test to find out.

You have been with the same company for five years but can get no further, and other people are now being promoted over your head. Do you:

1	a.	Quit and try a new job.	
	b.	Work even harder to gain the recognition you deserve.	
	c.	Complain to your boss that this treatment is not fair.	

You buy goods that are faulty and take them back to the store, but the sales assistant is unhelpful. Do you:

2	a.	Give the sales assistant hell until you get a more helpful answer.	
	b.	Go home and write to the manager giving detailed reasons for your complaint.	
	c.	Give up – you're obviously going to get nowhere.	

You are on an expedition in a remote area when you fall ill. Do you:

3	a.	Radio for a plane to pick you up.	
	b.	Push on regardless.	
	c.	Rest long enough to recover from your illness and then continue your journey.	

Your house is due to be demolished in an urban renewal project. Everyone else in the street has taken compensation and left. Do you:

4	a.	Hang on until the authorities carry you out by force.	
	b.	Take as much compensation as you can get and then leave.	
	c.	Leave under protest after having caused them serious inconvenience.	

You buy an old house that needs a lot of renovation. Do you:

score

a.	Work at it for some months and then lose enthusiasm.	
b.	Complete the job even though it takes many months of hard work.	
c.	Never quite get around to doing more than the essentials.	

5

You start a new job but find that your predecessor has left everything in a terrible muddle. Do you:

a.	Go to the boss and complain about your inherited problems.	
b.	Try to sort out the mess but tell everyone that it's not your fault.	
c.	Work persistently until you have the job in first-class order.	

6

You're learning to drive, but despite a couple of hours' hard work, you still can't master the three-point turn. Do you:

a.	Keep on trying until you get it.	
b.	Rush around the day before your test, trying to get everything done in time.	
c.	Have a coffee break and then give it another go.	

7

Your scientific research, the work of a lifetime, is called into question by new evidence from a fellow scientist. Do you:

a.	Accept the new evidence with as much grace as you can muster.	
b.	Reject the findings out of hand and continue with your own research.	
c.	Study the new findings to see if there are grounds for a new approach.	

8

You love someone who shows no sign of returning your affection. Do you:

9

a.	Keep trying – you could never love anyone else.	
b.	Give up – someone else will come along soon.	
c.	Keep trying, but keep an eye open for a more receptive lover.	

You have been trying for years without success to set a new record for the hundred-meter dash. Do you:

10

a.	Decide to try a less demanding event.	
b.	Train hard and give it one last go.	
c.	Vow to carry on until you get what you've aimed for.	

You are old and your relatives want you to go into a home where you can be looked after. Do you:

11

a.	Accept their decision as being for the best.	
b.	Vow to stay in your own home even if it's the death of you.	
c.	Accept a compromise of sheltered accommodation.	

You're a military commander and have been trying to take an enemy position for days, with much loss of life to your own side. Do you:

12

a.	Withdraw and try to find another route.	
b.	Keep attacking even though the cost is very high.	
c.	Radio HQ for new orders.	

You play chess but find that there is just one player in your club you can never beat. Do you:

13

		score
a.	Decide you will never be that good.	
b.	Study and practice hard to become good enough to beat this person.	
c.	Keep trying, but without much hope of success.	

You have tried to pass the same exam three times but have not succeeded. Do you:

14

a.	Decide to give it one last try before giving up.	
b.	Keep trying. You'll succeed or die in the attempt.	
c.	Give up and try something else.	

You have been trying to teach your child a foreign language but she is not interested. Every lesson becomes a battlefield. Do you:

15

a.	Persist – she'll be grateful to you one day.	
b.	Wait until she gets older and have another go.	
c.	Abandon the idea – she is obviously not a linguist.	

You go to the sales but find there is a huge crowd struggling for the bargains. Do you:

16

a.	Decide to see a movie instead.	
b.	Work your way to the front of the crowd no matter how long it takes.	
c.	Satisfy yourself with some minor bargains that require less effort.	

You discover that you have an incurable illness. Do you: **score**

a.	Fight it all the way – doctors have been known to be wrong.	
b.	Put your affairs in order and say goodbye to your loved ones.	
c.	Hope that your health will improve, but make preparations for the worst.	

Which of these statements applies to you most:

a.	Do or die.	
b.	Take the path of least resistance.	
c.	Do your best for as long as you can.	

Do you believe that he who fights and runs away lives to fight another day?

a. No.	**b.** Maybe.	**c.** Yes.	

Do you believe that you can't fight City Hall?

a. No.	**b.** Maybe.	**c.** Yes.	

Do you think it's sometimes better to give up than suffer too much hardship.

a. Yes.	**b.** Maybe.	**c.** No.	

Is it important to finish a race even though you have no chance of winning?

22

a. No.	**b.** Yes.	**c.** Maybe.	

How far would you defend a point of principle?

a.	Until it became inconvenient.	
b.	To the death.	
c.	Until I couldn't bear the strain any more.	

Do you think tenacity is an admirable quality?

24

a. Of course.	**b.** It's OK.	**c.** No.	

Would you consider running a marathon (assuming you could cope physically)?

a. Never.	**b.** It would be fun.	**c.** I might.	

Scoring

For each answer score the number of points indicated.

1. a:1, b:3, c:2	**8.** a:1, b:3, c:2	**15.** a:3, b:2, c:1	**22.** a:1, b:3, c:2
2. a:3, b:2, c:1	**9.** a:3, b:1, c:2	**16.** a:1, b:3, c:2	**23.** a:1, b:3, c:2
3. a:1, b:3, c:2	**10.** a:1, b:2, c:3	**17.** a:3, b:1, c:2	**24.** a:3, b:2, c:1
4. a:3, b:1, c:2	**11.** a:1, b:3, c:2	**18.** a:3, b:1, c:2	**25.** a:1, b:3, c:2
5. a:2, b:3, c:1	**12.** a:1, b:3, c:2	**19.** a:3, b:2, c:1	
6. a:1, b:2, c:3	**13.** a:1, b:3, c:2	**20.** a:3, b:2, c:1	
7. a:3, b:1, c:2	**14.** a:2, b:3, c:1	**21.** a:1, b:2, c:3	

Over 65

The maximum score is 75. If you scored over 65 you're a pretty tenacious character. In fact you hang on more than the average limpet. This is very admirable in some ways, but people might find your insistence on never giving in a trifle wearing.

55–64

If you scored in the range 55–64 you're still quite tenacious and certainly not a person to give in without a struggle, but on the other hand you're quite realistic about your limits.

45–54

If you scored in the 45–54 range you're not a pushover, but you won't struggle hard unless you see a very good reason to do so.

35–44

A score in the 35–44 range indicates a certain lack of tenacity. You're the sort of person who likes an easy life when you can get it.

Below 35

A score below 35 really shows a lack of staying power. You're the sort of person who likes things to be easy, and if they're not, you quickly lose interest.

Test Eleven

Are you brave?

This is a test of both physical and moral courage. In each situation you are given three choices of action and you must choose only one. Keep a note of your choices and compare them with the scoring key at the end of the test.

You see a child in difficulty at the swimming pool. You are not that good a swimmer yourself, but the situation seems desperate. Do you:

score

a.	Jump in anyway and hope that you will be able to cope.	
b.	Run for the lifeguard even though it might be too late when you get back.	
c.	Try to throw the child a rope.	

You're taking a walk in the country when you pass a farmyard guarded by fierce dogs. To your horror they are able to get out of the yard, and run towards you growling and barking. Do you:

a.	Shout at them to sit down.	
b.	Freeze.	
c.	Run.	

You have taken important exams but do not feel confident about the results. When the dreaded letter comes do you:

a.	Open it immediately to see the worst.	
b.	Get someone else to open it and read it to you.	
c.	Put off opening it until later.	

You witness an armed robbery in progress. Do you:

a.	Run to call the police.	
b.	Try to apprehend the criminals yourself.	
c.	Hide in a nearby shop until the danger is past.	

You are driving and you see a truck weaving dangerously along the road ahead. The driver is either ill or drunk. Do you:

5

score

a.	Pull in and call the police.	
b.	Flash your lights and try to get the driver to stop.	
c.	Keep well back out of danger.	

Your mother-in-law keeps interfering in your marriage until the point where you have finally had as much as you can take. However, she is known for her fearsome temper. Do you:

6

a.	Try to explain tactfully that her attitude is causing problems.	
b.	Let her have it. Pour out in one torrent all the anger and frustration of the last 10 years.	
c.	Think better of it and go outside to chop some wood while you calm down.	

You take your kids swimming. The other parents are all diving and your kids want you to join in, but you've never done it before. Do you:

7

a.	Explain that you don't feel confident enough to dive.	
b.	Shut your eyes and chuck yourself off the diving board	
c.	Make an excuse that you aren't feeling well.	

You go with your partner to a congress in Tokyo. You don't speak a word of Japanese and you have never visited the city before. While your partner is involved in business, do you:

8

a.	Stay in the hotel and amuse yourself as best you can.	
b.	Take a guided tour.	
c.	Set out to explore the city on your own.	

You are taking part in an amateur dramatic production when the star is suddenly taken ill. Horror of horrors, the understudy has failed to turn up as well! You know the part backwards though you have never performed it, being new to the company and having only a small role. Do you:

9

a.	Keep quiet and let them find someone who can muddle through.	
b.	Announce confidently that you will save the day.	
c.	Mention casually that you have read the part and hope that they will beg you to give it a try.	

You suffer from arachnophobia. You are alone in the house when you come across a huge spider. Do you:

10

a.	Beat it to death with something heavy.	
b.	Master your fear and, having trapped it in a glass, throw it out of the window.	
c.	Rush out of the house and refuse to return until someone comes home who can catch the spider.	

At a meeting of your school's PTA you are appalled to hear a friend of yours accused behind her back of being a bad parent. Do you:

11

a.	Loudly stand up for your friend in front of the other parents.		
b.	Say nothing.		
c.	Keep quiet at the meeting but tell your friend privately what you heard.		

Your child is terrified of dental treatment, a fear that you share. However, she needs an appointment with the dentist. Do you:

12

a.	Sit with her and try to comfort her while the dentist is at work.		
b.	Let her watch you having your treatment first to give her encouragement.		
c.	Push her into the surgery and retire to the waiting room hoping for the best.		

On an office outing everyone decides to have a go on a white-knuckle ride. Do you:

13

a.	Jump at the idea enthusiastically and encourage others to join in the fun.		
b.	Remember something you have left behind and rush off to look for it.		
c.	Grit your teeth and have a go even though you're terrified.		

You and your family are flying home from holiday when the plane runs into bad weather. The turbulence is the worst you have ever experienced and everyone is terrified the plane will crash.
Do you:

14

a.	Remain calm and try to encourage your family to do the same.	
b.	Clutch your loved ones to you and wait helplessly for the end.	
c.	Find a stewardess and ask her for reassurance that everything will be all right.	

You are ill and suspect that your condition may be serious despite what the doctors tell you. Do you:

15

a.	Make yourself believe your doctors.	
b.	Ask a close relative for 'the truth' even though you are aware they are unlikely to give it.	
c.	Demand that the doctors tell you the worst.	

You awake in the night to hear a noise downstairs. You think you may have burglars. Do you:

16

a.	Barricade the bedroom door and stay quiet until they have gone.	
b.	Tiptoe downstairs and attempt to phone the police without being overheard.	
c.	Take a heavy stick and charge downstairs to sort them out.	

You run into serious debt and the bank manager summons you to explain. Do you: **score**

17	a.	Keep making excuses to avoid a meeting.	
	b.	Meet him, explain the situation fully and ask what he will do to help.	
	c.	Meet him and grovel.	

You see a crowd of white youths surrounding some black kids and shouting threats and racist taunts. Do you:

18	a.	Cross the road and walk away.	
	b.	Go to find a police officer.	
	c.	Shout at the crowd to stop what they are doing.	

You go deep-sea fishing. To your amazement you find you've hooked a large shark. Do you:

19	a.	Fight it to the very last to reel it in.	
	b.	Cut it loose as quickly as possible.	
	c.	Make a token effort to land it but feel secretly relieved when it gets away.	

While trying to get on a bus you are pushed out of the way by a man who is much bigger than you. Do you:

20	a.	Take a step back to avoid a confrontation.	
	b.	Push your way in front of him and risk a fight.	
	c.	Point out to him politely that you were ahead of him.	

New neighbors move in next door, and you soon discover just how much they enjoy loud music. Do you:

a.	Ignore it and hope that they will improve with time.	
b.	Walk right round to their front door and complain.	
c.	Take an opportunity to bump into them as though by accident and point out tactfully that the music is too loud.	

21

You work as a research scientist and have been pursuing your pet project for 20 years. To your dismay a piece of evidence turns up that completely undermines all your work. Do you:

a.	Pretend that the evidence does not exist and carry on as though nothing had happened.	
b.	Write to a leading scientific journal and announce the failure of your project quoting the evidence in full.	
c.	Keep working and try to uncover other evidence that would be more acceptable.	

22

Driving on a lonely road at night you accidentally run over and kill a tramp. Do you:

a.	Drive on. Nobody is going to make a big fuss about a dead tramp anyway.	
b.	Drive to the nearest town and call the police anonymously.	
c.	Find a phone, summon the police and take responsibility for the accident.	

23

Looking through old papers, you discover your birth certificate which reveals that you were adopted. Your adoptive parents are now elderly and clearly intended that you should never know the facts of your birth. Do you:

24

		score
a.	Put the paper back and pretend you never found it.	
b.	Go straight to your adoptive parents and demand the facts.	
c.	Hint gently that you have some misgivings about your origins and hope that they decide to explain.	

Your son asks you about your involvement in a long-distant war. The truth is that you dodged the draft because you were scared. Do you:

25

a.	Say you refused to go as a matter of principle.	
b.	Lie about your military career.	
c.	Tell the truth and explain that war is something people should be scared of.	

Scoring

For each answer score the number of points indicated.

1. a:3, b:1, c:2	**8.** a:1, b:2, c:3	**15.** a:1, b:2, c:3	**22.** a:1, b:3, c:2
2. a:3, b:2, c:1	**9.** a:1, b:3:c:2	**16.** a:1, b:2, c:3	**23.** a:1, b:2, c:3
3. a:3, b:2, c:1	**10.** a:3, b:2, c:1	**17.** a:1, b:3, c:2	**24.** a:1, b:3, c:2
4. a:2, b:3, c:1	**11.** a:3, b:1, c:2	**18.** a:1, b:2, c:3	**25.** a:2, b:1, c:3.
5. a:2, b:3, c:1	**12.** a:2, b:3, c:1	**19.** a:3, b:1, c:2	
6. a:2, b:3, c:1	**13.** a:3, b:1, c:2	**20.** a:1, b:3, c:2	
7. a:2, b:3, c:1	**14.** a:3, b:1, c:2	**21.** a:1, b:3, c:2	

70–75

If you scored in the 70s (75 is maximum) you are very brave in all circumstances. However, your tendency to plunge head-first into dangerous situations means your chances of a long life are less impressive.

60–69

If you scored in the 60s, you are still very brave but have also learned a certain amount of discretion. You do not just plunge in but tend to think a little before you act.

50–59

If you scored in the 50s, you are about average in your bravery. You are prepared to confront issues when there is a need, and you're not too concerned, but you weigh the consequences and don't act irresponsibly.

40–49

A score in the 40s would indicate that you are relatively cautious. Your personal safety and well-being are important to you, and you will think long and hard before you act in a threatening situation.

30–39

You dislike confrontation, and the possibility of physical danger or violence upsets you. You may not have the courage of your convictions, but at least you remain safe.

25–29

If you scored below 30, you are unusually nervous. You have very little courage, and may run away even if it meant leaving a friend in danger. People may badger you into doing things that you would rather not.

Are you focused?

The ability to concentrate is vital in all areas of life. Whether you are working, studying, playing sport or driving your car you need to be able to keep your mind on the job in hand. Many people find this difficult. They have a tendency to daydream even in circumstances where this could be dangerous. Test your own powers of concentration.

When ploughing through a difficult read, do you:

1	**a.**	Often find that you have to re-read a page because you didn't take any of it in.	
	b.	Take it slowly, stopping every few pages to ensure you know what's going on.	
	c.	Generally read a generous chunk before feeling your attention is lapsing.	

You're gazing out of the window during a long train journey. When considering what scenery you've just passed by, do you:

2	**a.**	Feel able to describe much of the landscape you've just passed through.	
	b.	Discover you drifted off and have no idea where you are.	
	c.	Have vague notions of the sights you've just witnessed, but in no particular order.	

During a heated discussion, you find yourself embroiled in a complicated argument. Are you most likely to:

3	**a.**	Lose your train of thought and stop to ask, 'Where was I?'	
	b.	Follow the argument closely, and stick to the subject matter rigidly.	
	c.	Lose interest after the first few exchanges of ideas.	

You're confronted with a lengthy logic puzzle. Do you:

4	**a.**	Attempt to solve it but put it aside when your brain refuses to function after the first ten minutes of intense thought.	
	b.	Persevere purposefully until it's fully solved.	
	c.	Refocus your thoughts on the problem when you find your mind wandering.	

After sitting through a rather tedious documentary, do you usually find:

5

a.	You've forgotten most of what you've just witnessed.	
b.	You can quote a detailed synopsis of the contents to interested friends later.	
c.	You absorbed the main points, but some details eluded you.	

You stop to ask a passer-by directions to the street you're searching for. After a rather lengthy explanation of the route, are you most likely to:

6

a.	Set off in eager anticipation, and find the required street without further ado.	
b.	Manage to follow the correct route for a short while before forgetting the next stage and having to ask someone else for directions.	
c.	Admit you didn't quite get all that, and request the passer-by to kindly repeat it all.	

Half an hour through a rather banal meeting with colleagues, you realize you're being asked a question. Would you generally:

7

a.	Have to ask them to repeat the question.	
b.	Throw together an answer which you hope fully answers the question you only half heard.	
c.	Launch into an answer that directly relates to the topic of concern.	

You're given a somewhat daunting project to conduct. Are you most likely to complete it: **score**

8

a.	Intermittently, picking it up every now and again, and pushing it aside when you get bored.	
b.	Efficiently by structuring your work carefully, and sticking to your schedule without further procrastination.	
c.	Just on time, having found it easier to sit down and focus as the deadline approaches.	

During a casual stroll to the local shop, a neighbor approaches and you stop for a chat. Are you most likely to:

9

a.	Literally bump into your neighbor before you realize it's her.	
b.	Spot her before she spots you.	
c.	Greet each other simultaneously.	

Background music is filtering into your work area, where you're trying to solve a complex problem. Are you most likely to find yourself:

10

a.	So focused you're not even aware of the music.	
b.	Distracted totally and in need of a break.	
c.	Conscious of the interference but able to focus on your work.	

Halfway through reading a rather convoluted legal document, you're interrupted by a friend who asks if you fancy a break. Would you:

11

a.	Stop willingly as your attention was drifting anyway.	
b.	Prefer to plough on as you'd like to get through it without being distracted.	
c.	Be in need of another break despite your previous two.	

When browsing through newspapers, do you find yourself: **score**

a.	Not really absorbing much of what you've read.	
b.	Wincing at all the grammatical errors you spot during your perusals.	
c.	Able to quote the major news of the day back to others afterwards.	

12

A relative is chatting amicably to you as you prepare some supper. Would you:

a.	Be able to conduct a coherent conversation while cooking up a tasty meal.	
b.	Find yourself unable to do both at once, taking twice as long to prepare the food.	
c.	Mutter a few token acknowledgements to your relative while re-reading the recipe you've been distracted from.	

13

Do you find deadlines:

a.	Difficult to meet, as you find it hard to consistently focus on the task.	
b.	A useful incentive – when you know you've got to have something finished by a certain date, you find it relatively easy to get it done	
c.	Normally unnecessary as you find yourself suitably motivated to settle down on a task and get it finished promptly without them.	

14

During an energetic bicycle ride, a pedestrian suddenly blocks your path. Are you most likely to have:

15

a.	Seen the pedestrian from some distance and slowed down accordingly.	
b.	Been rather rudely awoken from your day-dream and had to swerve to avoid calamity.	
c.	Slammed on your brakes just in time as you realized what was about to happen.	

Your mind wanders during a dreary talk you're attending. Do you find yourself:

16

a.	Unaware of your daydreaming until a sharp prod from your neighbor jolts you back to reality.	
b.	Able to refocus your attention quickly on the talk in progress.	
c.	Attempting in vain to focus, but quickly drifting off into your day-dream again.	

Two chums sit down behind you on the bus and engage in an animated chat. Is your attempt to read the latest blockbuster likely to be:

17

a.	A dismal failure as you tune in to the juicy gossip being regaled behind you.	
b.	A success: you remain totally engrossed in your novel.	
c.	A challenge – you find yourself having to re-read a paragraph every now and again.	

Do you find simple sums: **score**

a.	Calculable mentally if no noisy distractions abound.	
b.	Impossible to do in your head as you always get distracted by something else.	
c.	Easy enough to calculate mentally – you can block distractions out.	

A hectic morning presents you with a multitude of urgent tasks. Do you:

a.	Prioritize, concentrating entirely on one task at a time, working through the list methodically.	
b.	Switch constantly between tasks, unable to focus entirely on any particular thing.	
c.	Attempt to address the different problems in turn, but remaining somewhat distracted by unresolved tasks during the course of your work.	

Do long lists of instructions generally leave you:

a.	Informed and capable – you find yourself able to assimilate large chunks of information in a short time.	
b.	Rather muddled – you tend to get distracted during attempts to absorb instructions of a complex nature.	
c.	As uninformed as before – you're unlikely to even attempt to digest such wads of information in one sitting.	

At the end of a lengthy film boasting an intricate plot, are you likely to be the one:

a.	Others ask what happens as they've drifted off while you've remained alert.	
b.	Who has 'switched off' frequently throughout, annoying the others with constant pleas for explanations.	
c.	Who can generally establish the basic plot, though exact details often fall by the wayside.	

Would you tend to ascribe any failure to remember news someone has told you to:

a.	The fact that you weren't concentrating on what was said at the time.	
b.	Your poor memory – you were paying attention, but time eroded the memory and replaced it with something else.	
c.	A freak occurrence – you generally possess a competent degree of focus and retention.	

An unwelcome telephone call brings you the bad personal news you've been dreading. Next day do you find yourself:

a.	Wandering around in a daze unable to concentrate on anything.	
b.	Eager to find things demanding of your attention to take your mind off it.	
c.	Attempting to be distracted by jobs that need doing, but failing to focus wholeheartedly on the job in hand.	

A mild cold leaves you blocked up and miserable. Do you find trying to read your favorite magazine to be:

24

a.	A welcome distraction – you try and succeed in refocusing your concentration positively.	
b.	No help – you're determined to dwell on your discomfort and refuse to concentrate on anything.	
c.	A comfort, but your usual listlessness is exacerbated and you find it tough concentrating on anything for long.	

After a particularly gruelling day in the office, you attempt to hail a taxi in rush hour. Are your efforts:

25

a.	Futile – you're hindered by thoughts of the day, which distract your search for a cab.	
b.	Successful – you're focused on your search for a taxi, and will conduct a post mortem on your day later.	
c.	Promising until a scuffle breaks out across the road and your attention lapses momentarily, losing you that elusive taxi.	

Scoring

For each answer score the number of points indicated.

1. a:1, b:2, c:3	**8.** a:1, b:3, c:2	**15.** a:3, b:1, c:2	**22.** a:2, b:1, c:3
2. a:3, b:1, c:2	**9.** a:1, b:3, c:2	**16.** a:2, b:3, c:1	**23.** a:1, b:3, c:2
3. a:2, b:3, c:1	**10.** a:3, b:1, c:2	**17.** a:1, b:3, c:2	**24.** a:3, b:1, c:2
4. a:1, b:3, c:2	**11.** a:2, b:3, c:1	**18.** a:2, b:1, c:3	**25:** a:1, b:3, c:2
5. a:1, b:3, c:2	**12.** a:1, b:3, c:2	**19.** a:3, b:1, c:2	
6. a:3, b:2, c:1	**13.** a:3, b:1, c:2	**20.** a:3, b:2, c:1	
7. a:1, b:2, c:3	**14.** a:1, b:2, c:3	**21.** a:3, b:1, c:2	

The maximum score for this test is 75. A score in the high 60s or 70s suggests you are someone capable of focusing on the engrossing task at hand even if a frenzy of clucking chickens flutters past your desk.

50 and above is fairly average, with gripping activities claiming your attention until something more interesting or newer comes along. Easing down towards the mid-30s suggests a concentration level more akin to a child's. You're in need of constant flashing lights, excitement and change, as your attention span is largely momentary. Below that and you stand little chance of ever achieving very much without a great deal of re-reading and huffing and puffing. You're more of an expert in breaks than in the art of study.

Are you a thinker?

Do you prefer thought to action? People are often divided into 'thinkers' and 'doers.' The two groups are usually not very impressed with each other. The doers see themselves as practical, level-headed and sensible. They refer to the thinkers as daydreamers who may be well-intentioned but are quite useless at getting things done. The thinkers, of course, do not share this view. They see themselves as intelligent, serious-minded and reflective, and they view the doers as brash, shallow and immature. Try the following questions and see where you fit in.

1 Do you think before you act?

a. Always. **b.** Never. **c.** Usually.

2 Are you a quick worker?

a. Yes, very quick. **b.** I like to take my time. **c.** Fairly quick.

3 Are you introspective?

a. Yes. **b.** Sometimes. **c.** No.

4 Do you prefer using stairs to an escalator?

a. Always. **b.** Never. **c.** Sometimes.

5 Do you go jogging?

a. Occasionally. **b.** Never. **c.** Regularly.

6 Do you daydream?

a. Frequently. **b.** Hardly ever. **c.** Sometimes.

7 Do you plan an activity rather than just going ahead and doing it?

a. Usually. **b.** Never. **c.** Sometimes.

8 Do you take part in sports?

a. Often. **b.** Sometimes. **c.** Never.

8 Are you an early riser?

a. Always. **b.** Never. **c.** Sometimes.

		score

10 Do you work with your hands rather than your brain?

a. Largely. **b.** Partially. **c.** Not at all.

11 Do you wonder what life is all about?

a. Often. **b.** Sometimes. **c.** Never.

12 Do you rush about when busy?

a. Yes. **b.** Sometimes. **c.** No.

13 Do you enjoy doing puzzles?

a. No. **b.** Occasionally. **c.** Yes.

14 Are you a good talker?

a. Yes. **b.** No. **c.** Not bad.

15 Would you enjoy rock climbing?

a. No. **b.** Not sure. **c.** Yes.

16 Do you prefer an activity holiday?

a. Yes. **b.** Sometimes. **c.** No.

17 Would you like to belong to an amateur theatrical group?

a. No. **b.** Possibly. **c.** Yes.

18 Are you a white-collar worker?

a. No. **b.** Not applicable. **c.** Yes.

19 Are you good at mental arithmetic?

a. Yes. **b.** Not bad. **c.** No.

20 Are you a fast reader?

a. Yes. **b.** Middling. **c.** No.

21 Do you easily get depressed?

a. Yes. **b.** No. **c.** In between.

22 Do you enjoying playing chess?

a. No. **b.** Sometimes. **c.** Yes.

23 Do you like to gamble?

a. Sometimes. **b.** Yes. **c.** No.

24 Are you early for appointments?

a. Always. **b.** Sometimes. **c.** Never.

25 Do you believe that you could write a book?

a. Yes. **b.** Not sure. **c.** No.

26 Would you rather go for a walk than sit and read a book?

a. Never. **b.** Sometimes. **c.** Usually.

27 Could you build a shed?

a. No problem. **b.** Maybe. **c.** No way.

28 Do you repair broken objects immediately?

a. Always.　　　b. Sometimes.　　　c. Never.

29 Could you learn lines for a play?

a. No problem.　　b. Couldn't do it.　　c. If I worked at it.

30 Would you join a team of mountaineers?

a. Yes, I'd love to.　　b. I wouldn't dare.　　c. I'd certainly consider it.

31 Do you enjoy 'do-it-yourself' projects?

a. Yes.　　　b. Sometimes.　　　c. No.

32 Do you like making speeches?

a. Yes.　　　b. No.　　　c. Don't mind.

33 Do you like to exercise?

a. Often.　　　b. Sometimes.　　　c. Never.

34 Would you like to play bridge?

a. Yes.　　　b. No.　　　c. Uncertain.

35 Would you ride on a roller coaster?

a. Yes, with pleasure.　　b. No, I'd be terrified.　　c. I wouldn't mind.

36 Have you ever camped out all night?

a. Often.　　　b. Never.　　　c. Occasionally.

37 Did you excel at sport at school?

a. Yes.   **b.** No.   **c.** I did quite well.

38 Would you enjoy skiing?

a. Yes.   **b.** No.   **c.** Don't know.

39 Do you have help with gardening?

a. No.   **b.** Yes.   **c.** Sometimes.

40 Do you like poetry?

a. Yes.   **b.** No.   **c.** Sometimes.

41 Do you clean all your own windows?

a. Yes.   **b.** No.   **c.** Sometimes.

42 Do you like being outdoors a lot?

a. Yes.   **b.** No.   **c.** In between.

43 Do you sleep more than eight hours?

a. Sometimes.   **b.** Never.   **c.** Always.

44 Have you ever wanted to own a sports car?

a. Yes, frequently.   **b.** I've considered it.   **c.** Not my scene.

45 Would you enjoy an evening spent reading a good book?

a. Certainly.   **b.** Possibly.   **c.** Definitely not.

46 Would you volunteer for a moon trip?

a. Possibly.   **b.** Certainly.   **c.** Absolutely not.

47 Would you enjoy angling?

a. Yes.   **b.** No.   **c.** Don't know.

48 Do you wear smart clothes?

a. Sometimes.   **b.** Always.   **c.** Seldom.

49 Do you enjoy going to lectures?

a. Yes.   **b.** No.   **c.** Not sure.

50 Do you hope that you will be very rich?

a. Yes.   **b.** No.   **c.** Don't think about it.

SCORING

For each answer score the number of points indicated.

1.	a:1, b:3, c:2	**14.**	a:3, b:1, c:2	**27.**	a:3, b:2, c:1	**40.**	a:1, b:3, c:2
2.	a:3, b:1, c:2	**15.**	a:1, b:2, c:3	**28.**	a:3, b:2, c:1	**41.**	a:3, b:1, c:2
3.	a:1, b:2, c:3	**16.**	a:3, b:2, c:1	**29.**	a:3, b:1, c:2	**42.**	a:3, b:1, c:2
4.	a:3, b:1, c:2	**17.**	a:1, b:2, c:3	**30.**	a:3, b:1, c:2	**43.**	a:2, b:3, c:1
5.	a:2, b:1, c:3	**18.**	a:3, b:2, c:1	**31.**	a:3, b:2, c:1	**44.**	a:3, b:2, c:1
6.	a:1, b:3, c:2	**19.**	a:1, b:2, c:3	**32.**	a:3, b:1, c:2	**45.**	a:1, b:2, c:3
7.	a:1, b:3, c:2	**20.**	a:1, b:2, c:3	**33.**	a:3, b:2, c:1	**46.**	a:2, b:3, c:1
8.	a:3, b:2, c:1	**21.**	a:1, b:3, c:2	**34.**	a:1, b:3, c:2	**47.**	a:1, b:3, c:2
9.	a:3, b:1, c:2	**22.**	a:3, b:2, c:1	**35.**	a:3, b:1, c:2	**48.**	a:2, b:3, c:1
10.	a:3, b:2, c:1	**23.**	a:2, b:3, c:1	**36.**	a:3, b:1, c:2	**49.**	a:1, b:3, c:2
11.	a:1, b:2, c:3	**24.**	a:3, b:2, c:1	**37.**	a:3, b:1, c:2	**50.**	a:3, b:1, c:2
12.	a:3, b:2, c:1	**25.**	a:1, b:2, c:3	**38.**	a:3, b:1, c:2		
13.	a:3, b:2, c:1	**26.**	a:1, b:2, c:3	**39.**	a:3, b:1, c:2		

Over 125

The maximum score is 150. If you got over 125, quiet reflection holds no charms for you, and you would not know an introspective thought if it bit you. You are a great person for getting things done as long as someone else tells you what to do.

100–124

This range indicates that you are very active but not to the exclusion of all else. You are the sort of person who can be relied upon in a crisis, and you will also be able to consider the consequences of your actions.

60–99

A score of 60 to 99 suggests that you are much more at home in the realms of thought, but you are not hopelessly impractical and will be quite able to take action when you really have to.

Below 60

A score below 60 suggests that you don't really have much talent for action at all and are much more at home with a good book or an interesting idea. And why not? There's no shortage of people who want to rush around doing things, is there?

Are you stable?

Some people find themselves permanently at odds with life. They feel unwell for no good reason, unlucky, unloved and unappreciated. This is what is called emotional instability. Others are quite confident about their lives and are happy, healthy and feel loved. This test will indicate how emotionally stable you are.

score

1. Do you blush often?

a. Yes.   **b.** No.   **c.** Occasionally.

2. Do you suffer from tension headaches?

a. Yes.   **b.** No.   **c.** Sometimes.

3. Do you worry about your health?

a. Often.   **b.** Sometimes.   **c.** Never.

4. Do you feel that your life is meaningless?

a. Sometimes.   **b.** Never.   **c.** Often.

5. Do you worry a lot about little things?

a. No.   **b.** Yes.   **c.** Sometimes.

6. Do you sometimes feel that you get blamed unfairly?

a. Yes.   **b.** Perhaps.   **c.** No.

7. Do you feel that most people are luckier than you?

a. Definitely.   **b.** Possibly.   **c.** Not really.

8. Do you suffer from fits of remorse?

a. Sometimes.   **b.** Often.   **c.** Never.

9. Are you worried by untidy surroundings?

a. No.   **b.** A bit.   **c.** Yes.

				score

10 Do you smile and laugh often?

a. Quite often. **b.** Very often. **c.** Seldom

11 Do you consider yourself a happy person?

a. Not very. **b.** Moderately. **c.** Quite happy.

12 Is your life fulfilling?

a. No. **b.** Yes. **c.** Not bad.

13 Do you make satisfactory relationships?

a. No. **b.** Yes. **c.** Sometimes.

14 Do you have many friends?

a. Yes. **b.** Not that many. **c.** No.

15 Were your parents happily married?

a. Unsure. **b.** Yes. **c.** No.

16 Do you wish you were somebody else?

a. Often. **b.** Never. **c.** Occasionally.

17 Are you satisfied with your appearance?

a. Reasonably. **b.** No. **c.** Yes.

18 Do you feel that other people respect you sufficiently?

a. No. **b.** Yes. **c.** Unsure.

19

Do you often feel listless for no good reason?

a. Sometimes.   **b.** Never.   **c.** Often.

20

Do you think the future holds good things for you?

a. I hope so.   **b.** I doubt it.   **c.** I'm sure it does.

21

Have you ever thought that life is not worth the effort?

a. Yes.   **b.** No.   **c.** Sometimes.

22

Do you suffer from morbid fears?

a. Not really.   **b.** Yes.   **c.** Occasionally.

23

Do people take to you readily?

a. Mostly.   **b.** Seldom.   **c.** Sometimes.

24

Do you enjoy your job?

a. Yes.   **b.** No.   **c.** Unsure.

25

Would you change your life if you could?

a. Certainly.   **b.** Probably.   **c.** No.

SCORING

For each answer score the number of points indicated.

1.	a:3, b:1, c:2	**8.**	a:2, b:3, c:1	**15.**	a:2, b:1, c:3	**22.**	a:1, b:3, c:2
2.	a:3, b:1, c:2	**9.**	a:1, b:2, c:3	**16.**	a:3, b:1, c:2	**23.**	a:1, b:3, c:2
3.	a:3, b:2, c:1	**10.**	a:2, b:1, c:3	**17.**	a:2, b:3, c:1	**24.**	a:1, b:3, c:2
4.	a:2, b:1, c:3	**11.**	a:3, b:2, c:1	**18.**	a:3, b:1, c:2	**25.**	a:3, b:2, c:1
5.	a:1, b:3, c:2	**12.**	a:3, b:1, c:2	**19.**	a:2, b:1, c:3		
6.	a:3, b:2, c:1	**13.**	a:3, b:1, c:2	**20.**	a:2, b:3, c:1		
7.	a:3, b:2, c:1	**14.**	a:1, b:2, c:3	**21.**	a:3, b:1, c:2		

Over 70

Maximum score is 75. If you scored over 70, you are showing signs of being deeply unhappy with your life. As these tests are not in any way scientific, it would be silly to base an important decision on the outcome, but since you seem so deeply depressed, you should probably see your doctor.

55–69

A score of 55 to 69 indicates quite a high degree of instability and might indicate that you really feel at odds with what is going on in your life. Some serious consideration of your problems could be required.

45–54

A score of 45 to 54 is reasonable but still shows that you have areas of your life where you are quite unhappy. You might benefit from some professional help in dealing with your problems.

35–44

A score of 35 to 44 denotes a stable and well-adjusted individual. You have your worries but, by and large, you know how to take care of them.

30–34

A score of 30 to 34 indicates someone who is really very stable and has life well under control.

Below 30

A score below 30 is to be deeply envied. Nothing at all takes the shine off your life and the rest of us can only stand by in helpless admiration.

Test Fifteen

Are you loyal?

Loyalty is always prized as a great virtue but, sadly, is often hard to find. How often have you discovered that people will not do for you what you would be willing to do for them? Are you the sort of person who sticks by your friends no matter what, or would you rather assess each situation as it comes and decide what is the best move for you? This test is designed to find out just how loyal you are prepared to be.

You have arranged to meet an old friend, but a good business opportunity comes up unexpectedly on the same day. Do you:

1

a.	Phone your friend and explain why you can't make it.	
b.	Try to rearrange the business appointment.	
c.	Get your secretary to phone your friend and make an excuse.	

You're talking with a group of people you really like when, to your surprise, they start to criticize one of your friends. Do you:

2

a.	Come loudly to your friend's defence.	
b.	Say nothing but decide to ignore their criticisms.	
c.	Decide that your friend may have faults you had not recognized.	

Do you always vote for the same political party?

3

a. Usually.	b. I like to decide each time.	c. Always.	

Do you prefer dogs to cats?

4

a. Yes.	b. No.	c. Not sure.	

Would you continue to shop at a local store if a supermarket opened up down the road?

5

a.	I'd go where things were cheapest.	
b.	I'd still go to the local store sometimes.	
c.	I'd stay with my local store.	

You are in the army and have been sent to fight in a war of which you disapprove. Do you:

6

a.	Desert.	
b.	Express your disapproval but continue to do your duty.	
c.	Get on with the job despite your private misgivings.	

You have been married for years, but have now fallen in love with a younger person. Do you:

7

a.	Have a brief fling that you keep secret from your partner.	
b.	Leave your partner for the new person in your life.	
c.	Give up this affair and stay with your partner.	

You have been in the same job for 20 years when a new opportunity suddenly comes your way. Do you:

8

a.	Grab the new job with alacrity.	
b.	Weigh up all the pros and cons before coming to a rational decision.	
c.	Decide you can't possibly leave your old firm, friends and colleagues.	

Your beloved dog falls ill. The vet's bills are terrific. Do you:

9

a.	Pay up, even though it hurts you financially.	
b.	Have the dog put down.	
c.	Get the vet to give you a cool assessment of the dog's chances before making a decision.	

Your best friend is found guilty of a serious crime. Do you:

10

a.	Accept the court's verdict and break off contact with your friend.
b.	Accept that your friend is guilty but try to offer support for old time's sake.
c.	Refuse to acknowledge the verdict and battle for your friend's release.

Do you support a regular sports team regardless of their results?

11

a.	I'd never change my team.
b.	I don't support anyone in particular.
c.	I sometimes change allegiance.

Do you believe in the saying, 'My country right or wrong'?

12

a. No.	**b.** To some extent.	**c.** Yes.

Do you believe that blood is thicker than water?

13

a. Yes.	**b.** No.	**c.** Not sure.

You win a lot of money in a lottery. Do you:

14

a.	Detach yourself from your old friends because they cannot share your new world.
b.	Try to keep in touch with people you used to know.
c.	Make sure your friends continue to surround you, and share your good fortune with them.

You discover that your partner has been having an affair.
Do you: score

15

a.	Throw them out.	
b.	Insist on a trial separation to see if you still care for each other.	
c.	Do everything you can to hold on to the one you love.	

16

Do you ever go to old school or work reunions?

a. Frequently.	b. Never.	c. Sometimes.	

17

Do you always buy the same daily newspaper?

a. No.	b. Usually.	c. Yes.	

18

Do you have many friends who have known you for most of your life?

a. No.	b. Yes.	c. A few.	

19

Do you keep in touch with distant relations even though you do not much enjoy their company?

a.	I make a point of it.	
b.	I try not to see them more than I have to.	
c.	I contact them when I can.	

20

Would you die for the sake of your friends?

a. Perhaps.	b. Certainly.	c. Probably not.	

A long-term employee of your company is caught pilfering office stationery. Do you:

21

a.	Fire him immediately.	
b.	Give him another chance.	
c.	Give him a trial period before making a decision.	

You go regularly to the same restaurant. One day you get a bad meal there. Do you:

22

a.	Complain but give them another chance.	
b.	Decide to change restaurants.	
c.	Carry on going.	

How highly do you rate loyalty in your list of desirable characteristics?

23

a.	Very highly.	
b.	Quite highly.	
c.	There are many more important things.	

A friend is accused of a crime. You have no idea whether or not he is guilty. Would you lie to give him an alibi?

24

a. Absolutely not.	**b.** Perhaps.	**c.** Of course.	

A friend does something that harms you. Would you:

25

a.	End the friendship.	
b.	Try to find out the reasons before acting.	
c.	Feel hurt but continue the friendship anyway.	

Scoring

For each answer score the number of points indicated.

1.	a:2, b:3, c:1	**8.**	a:1, b:2, c:3	**15.**	a:1, b:2, c:3	**22.**	a:3, b:2, c:1
2.	a:3, b:2, c:1	**9.**	a:3, b:1, c:2	**16.**	a:3, b:1, c:2	**23.**	a:1, b:2, c:3
3.	a:2, b:1, c:3	**10.**	a:1, b:2, c:3	**17.**	a:1, b:2, c:3	**24.**	a:2, b:3, c:1
4.	a:3, b:1, c:2	**11.**	a:3, b:1, c:2	**18.**	a:1, b:3, c:2	**25.**	a:1, b:2, c:3
5.	a:1, b:2, c:3	**12.**	a:1, b:2, c:3	**19.**	a:3, b:1, c:2		
6.	a:1, b:2, c:3	**13.**	a:3, b:1, c:2	**20.**	a:1, b:3, c:2		
7.	a:2, b:1, c:3	**14.**	a:1, b:2, c:3	**21.**	a:2, b:1, c:3		

Over 65

Maximum score is 75. If you scored 65 or above, you are ferociously loyal. There is nothing you would not do for those you consider to be your friends. You even continue this loyalty when it is not deserved or reciprocated.

50–64

If you scored 50 to 64, you are very loyal and generally give your friends the benefit of the doubt, but you are not so blinded by loyalty that you cannot see faults.

40–49

If you scored 40 to 49, you are capable of being loyal but also have a streak of self-interest that makes you think twice before supporting a friend in difficulty.

30–39

If you scored 30 to 39, you are mainly interested in yourself and give very little thought to the needs of those who might have a claim to your loyalty.

Below 30

If you scored below 30, you probably have no idea what this test is about.

Test Sixteen

Are you ill?

How much do you worry about your health? Are you the sort of
person who only has to hear the symptoms of a disease to believe
that you suffer from it, or is your doctor a stranger to you? Try the
following quick test to see how you measure up as a hypochondriac.

Do you sometimes suspect you may have an ulcer?

1

a. Yes.	**b.** No.	**c.** Undecided.	

You read in the newspapers that people with gum disease are more likely to have heart attacks. Do you:

2

a.	Shrug it off as another crazy health scare.	
b.	Resolve to take more notice of dental hygiene.	
c.	Make an appointment to see your dentist straight away.	

Your partner notices that your hair is thinning. Do you:

3

a.	Take no notice – these things happen as you get older.	
b.	Spend a lot of money on the latest fashionable remedy.	
c.	Take up massaging your scalp in the hope that it helps.	

Do you weigh yourself frequently?

4

a. Yes.	**b.** No.	**c.** Undecided.	

Do you examine your tongue often?

5

a. Yes.	**b.** No.	**c.** Undecided.	

You read that frequent tooth-cleaning is an important part of staying healthy. Do you:

6

a.	Start to clean your teeth three times a day.	
b.	Make no change to your current regimen.	
c.	Resolve to clean your teeth better in future.	

You see something on television about the benefits of eating oily fish. Do you:

score

7

a.	Take no notice – you don't like fish much.	
b.	Make sure you eat it regularly.	
c.	Decide you might eat it when you remember.	

If you were to get heart palpitations, would you:

8

a.	Assume you were suffering from heart disease.	
b.	Decide you were stressed and needed a holiday.	
c.	Not worry about the cause.	

If a friend recommended a faith healer would you:

9

a.	Dismiss the whole thing as nonsense.	
b.	Wonder whether there might be something in it.	
c.	Make a careful note of the details for future use.	

An expert suggests that you should have a first-aid box in your car. Do you:

10

a.	Ignore the suggestion.	
b.	Think it's a good idea but never get round to buying one.	
c.	Go and buy one straightaway and make sure it is always in place.	

If someone says that you seem to have lost weight recently, do you:

11

a.	Accept it as a compliment.	
b.	Wonder what could have caused the weight loss.	
c.	Assume that you must be ill.	

Do you get dizzy turns?   score

| a. Never. | b. Sometimes. | c. Frequently. | |

12

Do you consider yourself to be a healthy person?

a.	Yes, I'm never ill.	
b.	I try not to bother the doctor.	
c.	I've had health problems all my life.	

13

Do you follow a diet:

| a. Always. | b. When I get a bit overweight. | c. Never. | |

14

Do you watch medical documentaries on television?

| a. Avidly. | b. Occasionally. | c. Seldom. | |

15

Do you consult a 'Family Doctor' book or site about your symptoms?

| a. Regularly. | b. Occasionally. | c. Never. | |

16

Do you carry painkillers on your person just in case you are ill?

| a. Never. | b. Sometimes. | c. Always. | |

17

Are you afraid of coming into contact with infectious diseases?

a.	Not at all.	
b.	Only in areas where disease is widespread.	
c.	Always.	

18

You notice a strange spot on your skin that you have not seen before. Do you:

a.	Take no notice – after all, it's only a spot.	
b.	Keep it under observation to see if it changes.	
c.	Rush to the doctor to tell him you suspect a malignant melanoma.	

19

When eating out do you:

a.	Worry whether the kitchen staff have washed their hands before touching the food.	
b.	Forget about health – you're here to enjoy the meal.	
c.	Only go to a place whose reputation you are happy with.	

20

When you think of your old age, do you:

a.	Assume that you will have a few problems but remain reasonably healthy.	
b.	Fear that you will become incapacitated and dependent upon others.	
c.	Never give the matter any thought.	

21

Do you get constipated for no apparent reason?

a. Often.	**b.** Never.	**c.** Seldom.	

22

Do you check your pulse?

a. Occasionally.	**b.** Frequently.	**c.** Never.	

23

Do you take vitamins?

a. Always.	**b.** Never.	**c.** Sometimes.	

24

Do you worry about your health?   **score**

a. Frequently.	**b.** Occasionally.	**c.** Never.	

Scoring

For each answer score the number of points indicated.

1.	a:3, b:1, c:2	**8.**	a:3, b:2, c:1	**15.**	a:3, b:2, c:1	**22.**	a:3, b:1, c:2
2.	a:1, b:2, c:3	**9.**	a:1, b:2, c:3	**16.**	a:3, b:2, c:1	**23.**	a:2, b:3, c:1
3.	a:1, b:3, c:2	**10.**	a:1, b:2, c:3	**17.**	a:1, b:2, c:3	**24.**	a:3, b:1, c:2
4.	a:3, b:1, c:2	**11.**	a:1, b:2, c:3	**18.**	a:2, b:3, c:1	**25.**	a:3, b:2, c:1
5.	a:3, b:1, c:2	**12.**	a:1, b:2, c:3	**19.**	a:1, b:2, c:3		
6.	a:3, b:1, c:2	**13.**	a:1, b:2, c:3	**20.**	a:3, b:1, c:2		
7.	a:1, b:3, c:2	**14.**	a:3, b:2, c:1	**21.**	a:1, b:2, c:3		

Over 60

Most of us imagine illnesses at some time or other, but if this becomes a habit it may well point to deep anxieties that have not been recognized and dealt with. If you have a score of over 60 (the maximum is 75), you have a problem. For once the answer might really be to seek the help of your doctor.

50s

A score in the 50s would suggest that you worry about your health quite a lot. Certainly you seem preoccupied with the idea that you may become ill.

40s

A score in the 40s is rather more realistic, although you still sometimes harbor unjustified concerns over your health. You perhaps could learn to be bit more positive about your health.

30s

A score in the 30s suggests that you have no real health worries but are sensible enough to recognize when there may be a genuine problem.

Below 30

A score below 30 would suggest that you are definitely no hypochondriac. You do not take your health very seriously; if you have a problem, it may be that you ignore vital early warning signals of impending illness.

Are you timid?

Are you the sort of person who doesn't like to make a fuss? Would you put up with bad service rather than make a scene in a restaurant? Do you agree with people, even when you privately think they are wrong, just because you don't like trouble? Sounds like you have a bad case of timidity. Of course, we all have moments when we prefer to take the easy way out, but for some of us it becomes a way of life. Nothing ever quite seems worth the trouble that making a fuss will cause. To gauge the level of your timidity, try the following questions.

Do you feel most relaxed when: **score**

a.	You are just in your own company.	
b.	You are with two or three family and friends.	
c.	You are at a fairly large social gathering.	

At a social function you are standing in a group of 4 to 5 people. Do you usually:

a.	Do most of the listening to the others' conversation.	
b.	Contribute to the conversation equally with the others.	
c.	Usually make all the running in the conversation.	

When communicating with someone on a one-to-one basis, do you feel more comfortable communicating by:

a. Letter.	b. Telephone.	c. Face to face.	

You are on a bus or train. Do you:

a.	Never start up a conversation with a stranger sitting next to you or opposite.	
b.	Occasionally start a conversation with them.	
c.	Usually try to start up some sort of conversation.	

Would you take part in a karaoke competition?

a. You must joking	b. Maybe.	c. Just try and stop me.	

185

6

How often do you tell jokes in the company of others?

a. Never.	**b.** Sometimes.	**c.** Often.	

7

You are walking down the street and someone is coming towards you who you vaguely recognize. Do you:

a.	Walk past and ignore them unless they speak to you.	
b.	Give them a glance and sort of half nod.	
c.	Speak to them and attempt to engage them in some sort of conversation to find out how you know them.	

8

How often do you speak at meetings?

a. Hardly ever.	**b.** Sometimes.	**c.** Very often.	

9

Do you ever chat up the opposite sex?

a. Never.	**b.** Occasionally.	**c.** Often.	

10

Would you ever take part in an amateur stage production?

a. No way.	**b.** I might if pressed.	**c.** Yes, I would love to.	

When meeting someone for the first time do you: **score**

a.	Feel awkward and nervous.	
b.	Feel at ease and interested in getting to know them.	
c.	Feel bursting to tell them all about yourself.	

At the end of a dinner party when saying goodbye to a guest of the opposite sex would you prefer to:

a.	Just shake their hand.	
b.	Shake their hand and pat them on the arm.	
c.	Shake their hand and kiss them on both cheeks.	

When having a one-to-one conversation with someone would you prefer to:

a.	Listen to them talking about what they have been up to.	
b.	Talk equally about what each of you have been doing.	
c.	Tell them mainly about what you have been doing.	

You are in a crowded lift. Do you:

a.	Keep yourself to yourself and hardly notice the other people.	
b.	Don't say much but usually have a good look at the people in the lift with you.	
c.	Usually try to make some witty remark to the other people in the lift.	

At a work-sponsored dinner you are sitting at the table with 20 other people. How much conversation do you make?

15

a.	I speak very little but listen to other people and get on with my meal.	
b.	Usually I speak mainly just to the people on either side of me.	
c.	I tend to make quite a bit of the general conversation round the table.	

You are walking along in the town centre and a television station is conducting random interviews with people on a certain topic. Do you:

16

a.	Turn in the other direction or cross over to the other side of the street to ignore them.	
b.	Say a few words for the camera if approached.	
c.	Go out of your way to make sure that they ask you.	

You work in an office and the company board chairman walks through. Do you:

17

a.	Keep your head down and hope he doesn't notice you.	
b.	Carry on as normal and speak to him if appropriate.	
c.	Make sure that you have some sort of conversation with him.	

You are attending a function at which some important and influential people will also be attending. What would you wear?

18

a.	What I would normally wear to any other function.	
b.	I would probably buy something new for the occasion.	
c.	I would make sure I wore something to make me stand out from the crowd.	

How often do you push for promotion at work?

19

a. Never.	b. Sometimes.	c. Often.	

How would you feel if asked to make a speech in front of a large group?

20

a.	Terrified at the prospect.	
b.	I would try to prepare and make a good job of it even though it was not something that I would choose to do.	
c.	I would be pleased and excited at the prospect.	

You are at a nightclub and the singer asks for volunteers to go up on stage to help him out with a number. Would you:

21

a. Never volunteer	b. Possibly volunteer.	c. Be up on stage in a flash.	

When you are worried about something do you:

22

a.	Bottle it up inside you.	
b.	Discuss it with close friends and family.	
c.	Discuss it with as many people as you can.	

Do you sunbathe in your swimwear in the back garden in view of the neighbors?

23

a. Never.	b. Occasionally.	c. Often.	

If you are in the company of people who start telling risqué jokes how do you react?

score

a.	I feel very embarrassed and wish they would shut up.	
b.	I don't particularly approve but am not embarrassed.	
c.	I match them joke for joke.	

If a rather loud verbal argument breaks out between two colleagues at work, do you:

a.	Keep your head down and leave well alone.	
b.	Perhaps try to calm things down if you think it wise to do so in the circumstances.	
c.	Almost always get involved either by joining in or trying to calm things down.	

Scoring

Award yourself 3 points for every (c) answer, 2 point for every (b) and 1 point for every (a) answer.

More than 55

You are brimming with self-confidence, but you should be careful not to be extroverted to the point where people find you excessively pushy, even overbearing. Just remember at all times that your bubbly personality should be tempered with some degree of modesty and sensitivity toward other people.

35–55

You are no shrinking violet (even though you may sometimes think you are), but at the same time you don't push yourself beyond what to most people is an acceptable degree of behavior. You may secretly admire the way more extrovert people behave; but remember that it is these people who are in the minority and that, by showing a little reserve at the right time, you are probably regarded by other people as a much more appealing personality and someone they enjoy having in their company.

Less than 35

You are what some people would call a shrinking violet, but that's the way many people are, and it doesn't make you any worse a person than someone who is excessively outgoing. Many people are extremely modest and shy but at the same time have the ability to be high achievers in their own field provided that they can recognize their own talents and gain that bit of extra self-confidence to harness their potential.

Are you evasive?

Some people are noted for saying what they mean and meaning what they say. However, such people, though admirable, can be a little hard to live with. The unvarnished truth is often not quite what you want to hear. On the other hand, many people indulge in what psychologists call 'self-monitoring behavior.' These are the people who think a little before they speak, weigh up the effect their words might have on others and, if necessary, alter what they were going to say to something a little less controversial. They would think of this behavior as tactful and diplomatic; others would describe it as disingenuous or even sneaky. Try the following test and see if you are adept at self-monitoring.

1 Can you laugh convincingly at other people's jokes even if you don't find them funny?

a. No.   **b.** Yes.   **c.** Sometimes.

2 Would you start a political discussion with someone you didn't know well?

a. Yes.   **b.** No.   **c.** Unsure.

3 When political canvassers call at your door, do you express your real views to them?

a. Always.   **b.** Sometimes.   **c.** Never.

4 Would you make a good politician?

a. No.   **b.** Yes.   **c.** Unsure.

5 If you were discussing religion with someone whose views you did not share, would you:

a. Express your own views forcibly.

b. Try to find a compromise.

c. Give the other person the impression that you agreed with them without actually saying so.

6 Do you consider it more important to be truthful than to be tactful?

a. No.   **b.** Yes.   **c.** Sometimes.

7 Could you be successful as a second-hand car salesperson?

a. Unsure.　　　**b.** Yes.　　　**c.** No.

8 Do you agree with the statement, 'Everyone tells white lies now and again'?

a. Yes.　　　**b.** No.　　　**c.** Unsure.

9 Have you ever complimented someone on their appearance without really meaning it?

a. No.　　　**b.** Yes.　　　**c.** Unsure.

10 Do you listen politely to people with whom you deeply disagree?

a. Yes.　　　**b.** No.　　　**c.** Unsure.

11 Would you like to be a lawyer?

a. Yes.　　　**b.** Unsure.　　　**c.** No.

12 Do you expect people to take you at your word?

a. Always.　　　**b.** Seldom.　　　**c.** Sometimes.

13 Do you consider what answer someone expects of you before making a reply?

a. Unsure.　　　**b.** No.　　　**c.** Yes.

14 Do you value your reputation for straight talking?

a. Very much.　　　**b.** Not really.　　　**c.** Not sure.

15 Would you express your opinions even at the risk of being unpopular?

a. Yes. **b.** No. **c.** Perhaps.

16 Do you find it hard to know what your true opinion is?

a. No. **b.** Sometimes. **c.** Yes.

17 Is it important to you that people trust your word without question?

a. Unsure. **b.** Yes **c.** No.

18 Could you easily argue a case for and against the same proposition?

a. Yes. **b.** No. **c.** Unsure.

19 Are you a smooth talker?

a. Unsure. **b.** No. **c.** Yes.

20 Could you sell something you knew to be faulty?

a. Yes. **b.** No. **c.** Unsure.

21 Do you try to appear agreeable even to people you dislike?

a. Sometimes. **b.** Seldom. **c.** Often.

22 Do you think of yourself as outspoken and principled?

a. Yes. **b.** No. **c.** Unsure.

23 Would you keep the peace by telling people what they wanted to hear?

a. Yes.　　　　　**b.** No.　　　　　**c.** Maybe.

24 If you served on a jury, would you be prepared to stand alone against the decision of your colleagues?

a. Yes.　　　　　**b.** Unsure.　　　　　**c.** No.

25 Do you think of yourself as tactful and diplomatic?

a. Unsure.　　　　　**b.** Yes.　　　　　**c.** No.

Scoring

For each answer score the number of points indicated.

1.	a:1, b:3, c:2	**8.**	a:3, b:1, c:2	**15.**	a:1, b:3, c:2	**22.**	a:3, b:1, c:2
2.	a:1, b:3, c:2	**9.**	a:1, b:3, c:2	**16.**	a:1, b:2, c:3	**23.**	a:1, b:2, c:3
3.	a:1, b:2, c:3	**10.**	a:3, b:1, c:2	**17.**	a:2, b:1, c:3	**24.**	a:2, b:3, c:1
4.	a:1, b:2, c:3	**11.**	a:2, b:1, c:3	**18.**	a:3, b:1, c:2	**25.**	a:1, b:3, c:2
5.	a:3, b:1, c:2	**12.**	a:3, b:2, c:1	**19.**	a:2, b:1, c:3		
6.	a:2, b:3, c:1	**13.**	a:1, b:3, c:2	**20.**	a:3, b:1, c:2		
7.	a:1, b:3, c:2	**14.**	a:1, b:3, c:2	**21.**	a:2, b:1, c:3		

Over 70

Maximum score 75. If you scored over 70, you are very concerned about hiding your true feelings from others. You do not lie through malice, but you are unwilling to suffer the inconvenience of honest debate.

60–69

This range indicates that you are still very concerned not to cause offence, but might occasionally state an unwelcome truth.

50–59

This score suggests that you would rather be kind than truthful, but you are also capable of dealing with people honestly

40–49

You tend to be quite honest, and will say what you mean. However, you are aware that some opinions may be hurtful, and will soften your words to avoid trouble.

30–39

This score indicates that you are quite outspoken and do not care much whether people like what you say or not.

Below 30

This score indicates that you are very honest but have no tact at all. People will respect the fact that you tell the truth as you see it, but they may not like your bluntness.

Are you flexible?

Psychologists are often interested in the Rigid-Flexible dimension of behavior. Rigidity is what Freud referred to as anal behavior and is exhibited by people who are sticklers for detail and dote on rules and regulations. Those of a more flexible turn of mind are far less likely to let small matters upset them and regard rules as being at best no more than a guide to behavior. Naturally, people at either extreme of this dimension do not get on too well together. To find out just how rigid or flexible you are, answer the questions below and then refer to the scoring chart at the end.

You've arranged to meet a friend at a certain time one evening, and plan your time accordingly. An hour before going out, the telephone rings and your friend asks if you'd mind making it another evening as something else has cropped up.

Would you:

score

a.	Happily arrange another convenient time to meet.	
b.	Say that you would prefer to meet that evening and stick to the original plan.	
a	Reluctantly arrange another rendezvous, and feel rather at a loss as to what to do in the evening to fill your time.	

When planning a holiday itinerary, do you normally find that:

a.	You stick rigidly to the plan regardless of what else is on offer.	
b.	You make only a very sketchy plan as you dislike having to stick to a schedule.	
c.	You may alter your holiday itinerary if you find preferable alternatives.	

You discover with dismay that your train home has been severely delayed, and getting home is now a case of waiting or finding alternative transport. Do you:

a.	Resign yourself to a long wait.	
b.	Establish what the other options are and catch a bus home instead.	
c.	Opt to take a later train home, and arrange an impromptu visit to a friend living nearby.	

Your carefully planned dinner party menu faces an unexpected hurdle when a guest calls to inform you of a food allergy – alas, a food that is a core ingredient to the meal. Do you:

4

			score
a.	Stick to the original menu, and whip up a simple alternative for your troublesome guest.		
b.	Omit the problem ingredient, and concoct a tasty alternative not far from your original plan.		
c.	Apologetically inform your guest that your meal won't be to his liking, and suggest he visits on another occasion instead.		

Your daily routine is thrown into disarray when a long-lost cousin from Australia appears on your doorstep, asking to stay with you for a few weeks. Do you:

5

a.	Revel in the excitement, temporarily discarding your normal routine to accommodate your cousin.	
b.	Get dreadfully disorganized, running around for weeks as you try to cope.	
c.	Make a few minor amendments to your daily schedule, minimizing the disruption by encouraging your cousin to adjust to your lifestyle.	

A backlog of work at the office provokes a request from your boss to stay late one evening to help address it. Do you:

6

a.	Ask if she can wait a few days as you've made other immediate arrangements for after work that you're loathe to change.	
b.	Agree, albeit somewhat reluctantly, to stay later, amending your original plans accordingly.	
c.	Explain that you've made other plans you'd rather not change and compromise by working through a few lunch hours.	

Your hairdresser calls, explaining that your appointment has been double-booked, and asking if you would mind changing it to another time. Do you:

score

7

a.	Change your appointment under protest, demanding a discount to compensate for the inconvenience.	
b.	Refuse, stating that it's not your fault and either they or the other client will have to rectify the problem.	
c.	Agree amicably to find another mutually convenient time.	

A trip to the theater provokes acrimony when you arrive only to discover that there are no tickets available for your play. Do you:

8

a.	Opt philosophically to see a different play instead.	
b.	Slouch off home dejectedly, maintaining that you wanted to see *that* play and refusing to see any others.	
c.	Require some persuasion from your companions before agreeing to see an alternative play.	

You've arranged to go out for lunch with a colleague, having agreed on Italian food. When you meet outside the restaurant, she asks if you fancy going for Chinese food instead. Do you:

9

a.	Insist on the Italian – you've already worked out what you're going to eat.	
b.	Admit that you were looking forward to Italian food, but Chinese is fine.	
c.	Switch your thoughts reluctantly from a steaming bowl of pasta to a tasty sweet and sour – but only after a bit of persuasion.	

You're engrossed in an important project at work when a colleague asks if you could put it aside for a while and work on another task with him. Do you:

score

a.	Prefer to carry on with what you are doing, even if it inconveniences your colleague.	
b.	Request a few minutes to wrap up what you're doing, then switch your attention to the new challenge.	
c.	Establish the urgency of both tasks, and reluctantly agree to help your colleague for a while.	

10

You bump into a long-lost friend in the street who suggests going for a coffee to chat and make up for lost time. However, your carefully scheduled day didn't allow for such activities. Do you:

a.	Gush how you'd love to, and postpone your next planned activity.	
b.	Explain that you're rather tied up at the moment and consult your diary to find a time when you're free.	
c.	Declare it'll have to be quick so as not to ruin the rest of your plans.	

11

Just before leaving to go to a rather glamorous dinner party, the host calls to tell you the seating plan has had to be changed and ask if you'd mind terribly sitting next to somebody else. Do you:

a.	Object vehemently – you'd already worked out what to say to your original neighbor at dinner.	
b.	Declare it really doesn't bother you where you sit, and you are happy to fit into their new arrangements.	
c.	Suggest another arrangement that isn't too far removed from the original.	

12

Your good intentions to spend a productive afternoon gardening prove impractical when the skies open and rain pours down with no obvious inclination to stop. Do you:

13

a.	Reason pragmatically that it's just one of those things and quickly engross yourself in an indoor task that needs doing.	
b.	Wander around listlessly for a while before a telephone call inspires you to do something more productive.	
c.	Feel rather at a loss and betrayed by the weather, and attempt feebly to venture outside with each sign of brightening.	

Plans for a business meeting you're organizing fall into disarray when a key participant announces he's unable to be there. Do you:

14

a.	Feel rather aggrieved that you'll have to change the plans but eventually arrange another time when you can all meet.	
b.	Insist that he tries harder to rearrange his schedule so as to meet yours, and eventually bludgeon him into suiting you.	
c.	Without further ado establish a more convenient time when everybody can attend.	

Your plans to dash straight home after work, into a relaxing bath and enjoy a tasty supper fade when you receive a call from a distraught friend desperate for a sympathetic ear. Do you:

15

a.	Scrap your plans for an indulgent night in and agree to meet your chum for a commiseration drink.	
b.	Tell your friend you're more than willing to listen, but ask if she can come round to your home later once you've had a chance to unwind.	
c.	Explain that you've already made plans for the evening, and can she wait until tomorrow for a proper chat.	

When organizing a day-trip with friends, do you feel most comfortable when:

16

a.	A detailed schedule is established and attentively followed through.	
b.	The day loosely follows a basic plan, but nothing needs to be rigidly stuck to.	
c.	A thorough timetable of events is planned, but it can be adapted to individual requirements if necessary.	

A friend asks if he can borrow your computer to type up his CV, but you'd intended to use it yourself on that particular day. Do you:

17

a.	Suggest another day to lend it to him when you don't envisage using it.	
b.	Rearrange your own plans, as you can easily do something else instead.	
c.	Explain that you did intend to use it yourself that day, but try to accommodate both him and yourself by lending it for just the afternoon.	

A lucky win lands you with a dream holiday for two in Cyprus. The night before take-off, a telephone call informs you that the hotel is plagued with disease, and offers you various alternatives. Do you choose to:

18

a.	Stay in a nearby hotel (boasting the all-clear) as you're determined to lap up what Cyprus has on offer.	
b.	Venture to the Greek islands instead, getting all excited about the unexpected change in plan.	
c.	Postpone the holiday until the hotel is safe again – you want to get exactly what you're entitled to.	

Your 8am shower proves to be problematic when an unexpected guest comes to stay and needs to use the shower at the same time. Do you: **score**

19

a.	Agree that one of you will get up a bit earlier on alternate days and rush through your daily scrub.	
b.	Explain that you need to stick to your routine, so your guest will either have to rise earlier or forgo their shower.	
c.	Switch temporarily to a leisurely evening shower to help accommodate your guest.	

Does the prospect of change fill you with:

20

a.	Dread – you like what you know and prefer to stick to your set routine.	
b.	Keen anticipation – you dislike monotony and prefer to lead a less predictable, spontaneous life.	
c.	Some trepidation – you find it easier to face the known than the unknown, which demands a change of action or attitude.	

Do you consider yourself most to be:

21

a.	A stickler for rules and regulations.	
b.	Happy to adapt to changing circumstance.	
c.	Someone forever seeking compromise to minimize the need to adapt.	

Do you prefer to know what you're doing:

22

a.	On a daily basis – it helps to keep a diary of major commitments, but you're content to adapt if needs be.	
b.	Days in advance so you can form a plan of action, which you generally adhere to.	
c.	When it happens – that way you avoid the need to change plans if something else crops up.	

When booking your ticket for a lengthy train journey in advance,
do you:

a.	Make an open booking at no specific time so you're not tied down.	
b.	Pick a time when you plan to travel, but check the ease of changing times in case your plans are altered.	
c.	Decide exactly when you intend to travel, and ensure that your movements fit in accordingly.	

23

An outing to a museum proves to be unsuccessful when you
discover at the door that it's closed due to unforeseen circumstances.
Do you feel:

a.	Somewhat peeved, but agree with your companions to postpone the visit and go for a walk instead.	
b.	Angry and indignant – you hate your plans being disrupted.	
c.	Put out and at a loss – until a companion reminds you can reschedule your visit for tomorrow when the museum has re-opened.	

24

A friend has offered you a lift to the airport to catch your plane, but
an unfortunate breakdown leaves him stranded and you without
transport. Do you:

a.	Make alternative travel arrangements efficiently – you'd allowed enough time for a change of plan.	
b.	Feel bewildered and in a panic – you find it difficult to adjust to unforeseen circumstances.	
c.	Feel mildly anxious until your friend suggests someone else who may be able to help.	

25

Scoring

For each answer score the number of points indicated.

1.	a:3, b:1, c:2	**8.**	a:3, b:1, c:2	**15.**	a:3, b:2, c:1	**22.**	a:2, b:1, c:3
2.	a:1, b:3, c:2	**9.**	a:1, b:3, c:2	**16.**	a:1, b:3, c:2	**23.**	a:3, b:2, c:1
3.	a:1, b:2, c:3	**10.**	a:1, b:3, c:2	**17.**	a:1, b:3, c:2	**24.**	a:3, b:1, c:2
4.	a:2, b:3, c:1	**11.**	a:3, b:1, c:2	**18.**	a:2, b:3, c:1	**25:**	a:3, b:1, c:2
5.	a:3, b:1, c:2	**12.**	a:1, b:3, c:2	**19.**	a:2, b:1, c:3		
6.	a:2, b:3, c:1	**13.**	a:3, b:2, c:1	**20.**	a:1, b:3, c:2		
7.	a:2, b:1, c:3	**14.**	a:2, b:1, c:3	**21.**	a:1, b:3, c:2		

60–75

The maximum score is 75. With a score between 60 and 75 you're willing to adapt to others, but attention may be needed if you're muddling up your desire to be flexible with other people's need for someone they can push around.

40–59

In the 40s and 50s, you like to know what you're doing from day to day but are content to embrace the unexpected and change your plans at the last minute as long as it doesn't cause you too much inconvenience.

Below 40

Below 40 and you're nearing the danger zone where your largely inflexible outlook is hindering any chance of spontaneity and excitement. Anyone who interrupts your schedule should beware.

Are you tidy?

It might seem personal to ask how clean you think you are, but it's a fair question. As with other virtues, people like to think they possess cleanliness, and delight in speculating on others who don't. I was once getting off a plane from Chicago that had just landed in London when one of my American acquaintances observed that he couldn't wait to get into a good, hot shower. Another member of our group observed 'Don't hold your breath in this town, buddy!' Try the following test to see if you can claim to be clean.

You're drying the dishes and notice that one of them has not been properly washed. Do you:

1

a.	Put it back in the pile to be washed.	
b.	Wipe off the dirt with the cloth you're using for drying.	
c.	Give it a cursory wipe and pass it as done.	

You take your dog for a walk and it decides to relieve itself right in the middle of the footpath. Do you:

2

a.	Leave the mess where it lies.	
b.	Drag the dog into the gutter so that the path isn't fouled.	
c.	Produce your ever-ready poop scoop and clean up the mess yourself.	

You come home very late from a party and are so tired that you just want to go to bed. Do you:

3

a.	Get straight into bed without washing.	
b.	Force yourself to go through the whole bathroom routine even though you're desperate to get some sleep.	
c.	Give yourself a quick wash and promise to do a thorough job in the morning.	

You get up late for work and are faced with a rush to get there on time. Do you:

4

a.	Wash thoroughly even though it means going without breakfast.	
b.	Have a perfunctory splash and hope no one will notice.	
c.	Forget about washing, you just haven't the time.	

You've been digging in the garden when your partner calls you in to eat. Do you:

5

a.	Rush straight to the table – your hard work has given you a good appetite!	
b.	Meticulously wash your hands – you just can't be too careful about infection.	
c.	Get the worst of the muck off and then go to eat.	

Having been for a walk in the country, you come home and tread mud over the carpets. Do you:

6

a.	Forget about it. Someone will clear it up eventually.	
b.	Rush to get some stain remover.	
c.	Make an effort to remove the worst of it, then give up before it's all gone.	

You notice that the car hasn't been cleaned for some time and is now filthy. Do you:

7

a.	Take the earliest opportunity to take it to the car wash.	
b.	Forget it. It will only get dirty again soon.	
c.	Bribe the kids to clean it.	

One of your kids comes to the dinner table with dirty finger nails. Do you:

8

a.	Ignore it. Kids always look like that.	
b.	Suggest that in future it would be better to wash before meals.	
c.	Send the offender directly to the bathroom with instructions to clean them.	

You are about to go to an important appointment when you notice that your shoes need cleaning. Do you:

score

a.	Rub them furtively with your handkerchief.	
b.	Ignore it. Who's going to look at your shoes anyway?	
c.	Take time to clean them before you go.	

The water company digs up the main outside your house and for a week you can only get enough water to drink. Do you:

a.	Arrange with a neighbour to take showers in his house.	
b.	Don't worry. It's a bit like a camping holiday.	
c.	Reserve a little of the precious drinking water and use it to keep as clean as you can.	

You're doing a bit of home decorating. Do you:

a.	Cover the furniture very carefully to make sure it doesn't get paint on it.	
b.	Cover it as best you can, but you never manage to protect it entirely.	
c.	Don't bother much. You'll probably be able to rub the spots off later.	

You're eating doughnuts. Do you:

a.	Lick the sugar from your fingers with great relish.	
b.	Wash your hands meticulously when you've finished eating.	
c.	Wipe your hands on your handkerchief.	

Would you ever use your own handkerchief to wipe your child's nose?

13

			score
a.	Never.		
b.	Sometimes, if there wasn't anything else handy.		
c.	Why not? There's nothing wrong with it.		

Would you share a comb with someone else?

14

a.	Ugh!	
b.	If I had to.	
c.	Sure. What's the problem?	

In a restaurant you spot the waiter folding up used napkins and returning them to the table. Do you:

15

a.	Report him to the manager.	
b.	Ignore it – you hate to make a scene.	
c.	Resolve to write to the local newspaper's restaurant review section.	

While pinned to the dentist's chair with your mouth full of tubes you notice his assistant pick up a piece of equipment from the floor and hand it to him to use. Do you:

16

a.	Leap from the chair, spilling tubes in all directions, to protest.	
b.	Lie quietly and let it happen. What can you do with a mouthful of metal?	
c.	Not think twice about it. A little dirt never hurt anyone.	

A local restaurant gets prosecuted for poor hygiene.
Do you: **score**

17

a.	Resolve never to go there again.	
b.	Decide that since they've been prosecuted they must now run the safest place in town.	
c.	Decide to wait a bit and see whether your friends go again.	

A friend can't finish her meal and offers it to you. It's something you particularly like. Do you:

18

a.	Refuse, but with the greatest regret.	
b.	Refuse politely but firmly. You could never eat leftovers.	
c.	Eat it with enthusiasm.	

Could you wash in water that others had already used?

19

a.	Yes, no problem.	
b.	I'd rather die.	
c.	With reluctance, if there was nothing better available.	

Would you drink from a public fountain?

20

a. Never.	b. If you were really thirsty.	c. You do it all the time.	

Would you eat chicken with your fingers?

21

a. Yes. Why not?	b. No, that's gross!	c. Occasionally.	

22 Do you regularly disinfect areas of your house?

score

a. When I remember.	b. Without fail.	c. I seldom get round to it.	

23 Do you always wash your hands before a meal?

a.	Sometimes, but I'm not usually that dirty.	
b.	Yes, always.	
c.	No, I don't see the need.	

24 Would you refuse to keep a pet because you think they are unhygienic?

a. No.	b. I'd certainly think about it.	c. Yes.	

25 Would you let your dog lick your face?

a. Yes, often.	b. Certainly not.	c. Sometimes it's hard to prevent.	

Scoring

For each answer score the number of points indicated.

1.	a:3, b:2, c:1	8.	a:1, b:2, c:3	15.	a:3, b:1, c:2	22.	a:2, b:3, c:1
2.	a:1, b:2, c:3	9.	a:2, b:1, c:3	16.	a:3, b:2, c:1	23.	a:2, b:3, c:1
3.	a:1, b:3, c:2	10.	a:3, b:1, c:2	17.	a:3, b:1, c:2	24.	a:1, b:2, c:3
4.	a:3, b:2, c:1	11.	a:3, b:2, c:1	18.	a:2, b:3, c:1	25:	a:1, b:3, c:2
5.	a:1, b:3, c:2	12.	a:1, b:3, c:2	19.	a:1, b:3, c:2		
6.	a:1, b:3, c:2	13.	a:3, b:2, c:1	20.	a:3, b:2, c:1		
7.	a:3, b:1, c:2	14.	a:3, b:2, c:1	21.	a:1, b:3, c:2		

70 or More

The maximum score is 75. If you scored 70 or over you are obviously very clean indeed. An exaggerated concern for hygiene is sometimes connected with neurotic, compulsive and obsessive behavior.

60s

A score in the 60s would suggest a very active concern for hygiene which, whilst laudable, might make you a little hard to live with.

50s

A score in the 50s suggests a more free and easy approach. You are certainly no slob but, on odd occasions and for good reason, you are willing to let matters slide just a bit.

40s

If you scored in the 40s you are really rather careless in matters of cleanliness, though you are at least aware of what you ought to be doing.

30s or Lower

A score in the 30s or below is too disgusting to contemplate!

Are you sunny?

If you are one of those who people who can leap out of bed and greet another day with a smile and a song this test is just your thing. We are looking this time for those who like to view life from the bright side. Of course, the rest of us will find you irritating, and may well say so in words that are chosen for their cruelty, but you will have the last laugh. Born optimists just sail through life seeing only the silver linings and barely noticing the clouds. The rest of us can only stand by and wonder. What is it with these people? Don't they see that the world is full of problems? Don't they care that the rest of us are beset by doubts and worries? Apparently not. To see if you are one of the lucky ones try the following test.

What are your feelings at the end of a very enjoyable holiday? score

a.	Upset and slightly depressed that it's over.	
b.	Looking forward to the next holiday.	
c.	Refreshed and looking forward to getting home and catching up with all the news.	

1

It's your fortieth birthday. What are your feelings?

a.	The best years of my life are over.	
b.	I'm getting older but I'll just have to make the best of things.	
c.	Life begins at forty.	

2

You have been in perfect health for the past 10 years.
Do you think:

a.	It can't last.	
b.	I've been lucky for the past 10 years, let's hope I'm as lucky for the next 10.	
c.	I will work at keeping myself in good shape so that I will have a good chance of staying in good health in the future.	

3

You are going through one of life's bad patches. What is your philosophy on this?

a.	I seem to have more than my share of bad patches.	
b.	Life is harsh.	
c.	Life can be cruel at times but this bad patch won't last forever.	

4

You have just been made redundant without any warning.
What is your reaction?

5

a.	You feel like it's the end of the world.	
b.	You are upset and hope you can find another job quickly.	
c.	You are upset but think that it may give you the opportunity for change which may be for the best in the long run.	

You have a gamble on a big horse race. What are your expectations?

6

a.	Your horse will probably fall at the first fence.	
b.	You don't really expect to win but hope you get a good run for your money.	
c.	You work out your anticipated winnings even before the race has started.	

What would be your thoughts if someone said, 'Life is not a rehearsal'?

7

a.	It would have turned out a lot better than this if I had been able to rehearse it.	
b.	I don't agree – there is something better after this life.	
c.	It's a good job I am making the best of things.	

What is your attitude to taking chances?

8

a.	I don't take chances if it can be avoided.	
b.	I think it is necessary to take chances from time to time.	
c.	I like taking chances; it gives me a buzz.	

Why do you take part in sport?

9

a.	For something to do.	
b.	I like competing and I like the friendships that can be forged.	
c.	To win.	

What do you think if a decision goes against you that you can't reverse?

10

a.	Quite put out about it.	
b.	I try to see the other point of view.	
c.	I think that perhaps it might be for the best in the long run.	

You have come to the end of a relationship that really you would like to continue even though you accept it is not possible. What are your feelings?

11

a.	Devastated.	
b.	I will get over it one day but it will take a long time.	
c.	I must try to put this behind me quickly and get on with the rest of my life.	

What is your attitude to change?

12

a.	Change is never for the better.	
b.	Change, like death and taxes, is inevitable.	
c.	It's a whole new challenge.	

You are told that a giant meteor will strike the earth in 10 minutes and there is very little chance anyone will survive.
What is your reaction?

13	a.	I've got to die sometime, it might as well be now.	
	b.	Find your loved ones to say your goodbyes.	
	c.	Someone always survives, now what can I do to increase the chances of it being me?	

You are at one of life's crossroads and unsure which way to turn.
What do you think?

14	a.	Whatever I do it will probably be wrong.	
	b.	I wish I could go back instead of forward.	
	c.	Fate will decide, and whichever route I choose it will turn out for the best.	

You are going through a bad patch in a relationship. Do you feel:

15	a.	It looks like this is the end.	
	b.	Things are going from bad to worse.	
	c.	We will work things out.	

What is your reaction when someone talks about 'the good old days'?

16	a.	I agree, things were better in years gone by.	
	b.	There were good times in the past as there will be again.	
	c.	Generally things are getting better, and we have a lot of exciting times to look forward to.	

You and your partner seem to be developing different interests. Do you feel:

17

a.	That you seem to be growing apart.	
b.	You accept the inevitability of what is happening but wish you could share everything together as you once did.	
c.	You are pleased for your partner and feel that the different interests are all part of you both growing as individuals.	

What are your feelings about autumn?

18

a.	Slightly depressed that it will soon be winter.	
b.	No particular feelings, it's just another time of the year.	
c.	It's a beautiful time of the year.	

What do you think when you get the odd ache and pain?

19

a.	I tend to worry that it might be something serious.	
b.	I hope they will soon disappear but think that if they don't I will pay a visit to the doctor to be on the safe side.	
c.	I don't think too much about them. Little aches and pains come and go all the time.	

How much of a part do you think luck plays in one's life?

20

a.	A great deal.	
b.	Some people are luckier than others.	
c.	To a great extent you make your own luck.	

Imagine yourself in a dangerous life threatening situation like the characters trapped on the top floor in the movie *The Towering Inferno*. What are your thoughts?

21

		score
a.	This is it, I'm going to die.	
b.	How on earth did I get in this situation? It's like a bad dream.	
c.	When I get out of this I'll celebrate.	

You have just been dealt one of life's bitter disappointments. What is your reaction?

22

a.	It always happens to me.	
b.	You feel as though you have been kicked in the stomach.	
c.	Win some, lose some.	

You go out for a meal with friends and it turns out to be a disaster – you wait two hours to be served and all the food is cold. What is your reaction?

23

a.	Every time I go out to enjoy myself something seems to go wrong.	
b.	You and your friends come to the conclusion that you can't do anything about it as it's just typical in this day and age.	
c.	You have a good laugh about it but write to the restaurant to complain and hope you will be invited back for a free meal.	

You have a sudden windfall of $5,000. What is your reaction?

24

a.	$5,000 isn't going to get me very far these days.	
b.	I'm going to treat myself to some little luxury I haven't been able to afford up to now.	
c.	Good luck always comes in threes – another two to go.	

Your car skids out of control and ends up in a ditch upside down but you scramble out unscathed. What is your immediate reaction?

score

25

a.	Oh no, look at my car, it's a write-off!	
b.	This is bad luck, all that hassle with the insurance, and how long am I going to be without a car?	
c.	I'm lucky to be alive.	

Scoring

Award yourself:

3 points for every (c) answer

2 point for every (b) answer

1 points for every (a) answer

Over 55:

Maximum score is 75. Over 55, What a wonderful outlook on life you have! Not for you sleepless nights worrying about things that may never happen. You are the eternal optimist who always looks on the bright side whatever happens and firmly believes that every cloud has a silver lining. As long as you are not naive about life's potential to strike back with harsh realities then you are the envy of us all – carefree, but at the same time knowing that you can get the best out of life as long as you are prepared to accept the ups with the downs.

35–55:

Like the majority of people in the world, you are a realist. You know that life has its ups and downs, but hopefully the high points will exceed the low points and this is what really counts in the end. While you do not consider yourself to be a pessimist, perhaps you can learn a little from the eternal optimist and try not to worry so much. Remember that most of the things we worry about in life never happen anyway, so why worry about anything unless it actually does happen?

Less than 35:

You are a born pessimist. While this doesn't make you a worse person, and you can still be successful and have many friends, it does mean that you suffer from a great deal of inner turmoil and you are constantly nagged by doubts and worries about almost everything. You must try not to make mountains out of molehills and put negative thoughts to the back of your mind. Try to think of the positive side of life, for there are many people in a worse position than yourself. If you can do this – and it may take a great deal of effort on your part to achieve – you will start to feel the benefits, both healthwise and in an improved outlook on life in general.

Are you religious?

It is hard to decide what a question like 'How religious are you?' might mean. Religion means many different things to different people and, if you examine the subject globally, you quickly discover religious concepts in one culture that would be incomprehensible in another. As this book is written primarily for an English-speaking audience we decided that, for the purposes of this test only, we would consider 'religious' to refer to a traditional, fundamentalist belief in one God as revealed to us through Christian Scriptures. This is a view that should also be familiar to, even if not accepted by, Jewish and Muslim readers. A high score on this test would indicate a firm belief in those sorts of traditional religious values.

1

Are you a member of any established religion?

a. Yes. **b.** No. **c.** In name only.

2

Do you believe that prayers are answered?

a. Always. **b.** Sometimes. **c.** Never.

3

Do you believe that morality is divinely inspired?

a. No. **b.** Yes. **c.** Don't know.

4

Do you believe that we are punished for our sins?

a. Don't know. **b.** Yes. **c.** No.

5

Do you believe that virtue is its own reward?

a. No. **b.** Yes. **c.** Don't know.

6

Do you believe in life after death?

a. Yes. **b.** No. **c.** Don't know.

7

Do you believe that the world was created by God?

a. No. b. Yes. **c.** Don't know.

8

Do you believe that our actions are noted by God?

a. Don't know. **b.** Yes. **c.** No.

9

Do you believe in evil as an entity?

a. No. **b.** Yes. **c.** Don't know.

10 Can illness be cured by religious faith?

a. Yes.　　　　**b.** No.　　　　**c.** Don't know.

11 Do you believe that miracles occur?

a. Don't know.　　**b.** Yes.　　　　**c.** No.

12 Do you believe that God intervenes in the world?

a. No.　　　　**b.** Yes.　　　　**c.** Don't know.

13 Do you attend a place of worship?

a. Frequently.　　**b.** Occasionally.　　**c.** Never.

14 Do you believe that your life has been benefited by religion?

a. Yes.　　　　**b.** Unsure.　　　　**c.** No.

15 Do you consider the religious implications of the way you act in daily life?

a. Always.　　　**b.** Never.　　　**c.** Usually.

16 How important is religion in your life?

a. Not important.
b. Very important.
c. Quite important.

17 Do you consider that there is only one true religion?

a. Unsure.　　　**b.** Yes.　　　　**c.** No.

18 Do you read religious texts?

a. Often. **b.** Sometimes. **c.** Never.

19 Would you like the life of a priest, vicar, rabbi, etc?

a. Yes. **b.** No. **c.** Don't know.

20 Could you live without your religious faith?

a. Unsure. **b.** No. **c.** Yes.

21 Do you look to God for guidance in your life?

a. Always. **b.** Sometimes. **c.** Never.

22 Do you believe that science and religion are incompatible?

a. No. **b.** Yes. **c.** Unsure.

23 Does religious faith give you courage in difficult situations?

a. Always. **b.** Sometimes. **c.** Never.

24 Do you stick strictly to the tenets of your religion?

a. Rigidly. **b.** Not rigidly. **c.** I'm quite lax about them.

25 Do you have doubts about the existence of God?

a. Never. **b.** Sometimes. **c.** Always.

26 Do you ever doubt the teachings of your religious organization?

a. Often.　　　**b.** Sometimes.　　　**c.** Never.

27 Would a serious misfortune persuade you to abandon your religion?

a. No.　　　**b.** Yes.　　　**c.** Unsure.

28 Do you believe that there will be a day of judgement for all of us?

a. Yes.　　　**b.** No.　　　**c.** Don't know.

29 Do you see the hand of God in everyday events?

a. No.　　　**b.** Yes.　　　**c.** Unsure.

30 Would you be prepared to suffer for your faith?

a. Unsure.　　　**b.** No.　　　**c.** Yes.

31 Would you be prepared to die for your faith?

a. Yes.　　　**b.** Unsure.　　　**c.** No.

32 Is your religion the most important thing in your life?

a. Yes.　　　**b.** No.　　　**c.** Unsure.

33 Would you be prepared for your child to marry someone of another faith?

a. Unsure.　　　**b.** No.　　　**c.** Yes.

34 Would you consider marrying outside your religion?

a. Yes. **b.** No. **c.** Unsure.

35 Do you approve of interfaith marriage for other people?

a. No. **b.** Yes. **c.** Unsure.

36 Do you socialize with people outside your faith?

a. Often. **b.** Never. **c.** Sometimes.

37 Do you know much about other religions?

a. A lot. **b.** Not much. **c.** Nothing.

38 Do you believe comparative religion should be taught in schools?

a. Unsure. **b.** No. **c.** Yes.

39 Do you feel that your children should be taught about religion in school?

a. Yes. **b.** No. **c.** Unsure.

40 Would you let your children go to a school where other religions are taught?

a. No. **b.** Unsure. **c.** Yes.

41 Would you send your children to a religious school if one were available?

a. No. **b.** Yes. **c.** Unsure.

42 Could you accept a member of your family converting to another religion?

    a. Yes.   **b.** No.   **c.** Unsure.

43 Can you work happily alongside members of other faiths?

    a. No.   **b.** Unsure.   **c.** Yes.

44 Do you bring your beliefs into conversations with people you meet in your daily life?

    a. Often.   **b.** Sometimes.   **c.** Never.

45 Do you try to convert others to your beliefs?

    a. Sometimes.   **b.** Often.   **c.** Never.

46 Do you believe that members of other religions (or none) are damned?

    a. Yes.   **b.** No.   **c.** Unsure.

47 Would you listen to someone who tried to convert you to another religion?

    a. Yes.   **b.** No.   **c.** Unsure.

48 Do you approve of sex other than for the purpose of procreation?

    a. No.   **b.** Unsure.   **c.** Yes.

49 Do you feel that most people are sinful?

    a. Unsure.   **b.** No.   **c.** Yes.

50. Do you feel that moral values are not possible without religion?

a. Yes.　　**b.** No.　　**c.** Unsure.

Scoring

For each answer score the number of points indicated.

1. a:3, b:1, c:2	14. a:3, b:2, c:1	27. a:3, b:1, c:2	40. a:3, b:2, c:1
2. a:3, b:2, c:1	15. a:3, b:1, c:2	28. a:3, b:1, c:2	41. a:1, b:3, c:2
3. a:1, b:3, c:2	16. a:1, b:3, c:2	29. a:1, b:3, c:2	42. a:1, b:3, c:2
4. a:2, b:3, c:1	17. a:2, b:3, c:1	30. a:2, b:1, c:3	43. a:3, b:2, c:1
5. a:1, b:3, c:2	18. a:3, b:2, c:1	31. a:3, b:2, c:1	44. a:3, b:2, c:1
6. a:3, b:1, c:2	19. a:3, b:1, c:2	32. a:3, b:1, c:2	45. a:2, b:3, c:1
7. a:1, b:3, c:2	20. a:2, b:3, c:1	33. a:2, b:3, c:1	46. a:3, b:1, c:2
8. a:2, b:3, c:1	21. a:3, b:2, c:1	34. a:1, b:3, c:2	47. a:1, b:3, c:2
9. a:1, b:3, c:2	22. a:1, b:3, c:2	35. a:3, b:1, c:2	48. a:3, b:2, c:1
10. a:3, b:1, c:2	23. a:3, b:2, c:1	36. a:1, b:3, c:2	49. a:2, b:1, c:3
11. a:2, b:3, c:1	24. a:3, b:2, c:1	37. a:1, b:2, c:3	50. a:3, b:1, c:2
12. a:1, b:3, c:2	25. a:3, b:2, c:1	38. a:2, b:3, c:1	
13. a:3, b:2, c:1	26. a:1, b:2, c:3	39. a:3, b:1, c:2	

Over 125
Maximum score is 150. If you scored over 125, you are a religious traditionalist with no time for doubts, modern views, or anyone's opinions but those of your own faith. This may not be a popular position but, as you see your life being entirely guided by the will of God, you are not likely to care what others may think.

110–124
If you scored between 110 and 124, you are still very much influenced by traditional values but are not completely stuck in your views. You may even allow yourself to have doubts occasionally, though in the long run you are unlikely to lose your faith.

95–109
If you scored between 95 and 109, you are less traditional in your outlook but religion still plays an important part in your life. You are prepared to admit that religious issues

are far from simple and you might well contemplate views other than your own.

80–94
If you scored between 80 and 94, you are not much of a traditionalist and, in fact, you may well have considerable reservations about some religious teachings and practices.

65–79
A score between 65 and 79 would suggest that you have serious doubts about the value of traditional religious beliefs and would not describe yourself as 'religious' as we have defined the term.

Below 65
A score below 65 suggests that you have little interest in the subject and, when you do consider religious matters, you are extremely skeptical on most points. You certainly don't consider yourself to be a religious person in the traditional sense and you probably have little time for those who do.

Are you happy?

Do you greet each new day with a spring in your step and a song in your heart? Or is your life rather grey and lacking in sparkle? Happiness is one of the most important factors in mental health but it is hard to decide what gives rise to it. There are all sorts of material considerations like income, family relationships, contentment at work and so on that are clearly involved in how happy we are, but that is seldom the whole story. Some people have a sunny disposition despite their difficulties, while others manage to be miserable in spite of living in great comfort. Find out how you measure up by answering the following questions.

1 Do you wake up looking forward to a new day?

   a. Always.   **b.** Sometimes.   **c.** Rarely.

2 Do you enjoy your work?

   a. Not much.   **b.** A bit.   **c.** Very much.

3 Do you have many friends?

   a. Lots.   **b.** Quite a few.   **c.** Not many.

4 Are you in a stable relationship?

   a. No.   **b.** Yes.   **c.** Not at the moment.

5 Does the state of the world concern you?

   a. Sometimes.   **b.** Yes.   **c.** No.

6 Do you feel confident about your future?

   a. No.   **b.** Yes.   **c.** Fairly.

7 Do you worry about political issues?

   a. Never.   **b.** Sometimes.   **c.** Frequently.

8 Are you financially secure?

   a. Fairly.   **b.** Yes.   **c.** No.

9 Do you have interests apart from your work?

   a. Many.   **b.** Some.   **c.** Few.

10 Do you bear your troubles cheerfully?

   a. No.   **b.** Unsure.   **c.** Yes.

11 Do you suffer from fits of anxiety?

   a. Sometimes.   **b.** Often.   **c.** Rarely.

12 Do you have a religious faith of any sort?

   a. Yes.   **b.** Unsure.   **c.** No.

13 Do you feel that the world is a safe place to bring children into?

a. No. **b.** Yes. **c.** Unsure.

14 Do you feel lonely?

a. Often. **b.** Sometimes. **c.** Seldom.

15 Would you like to change lives with someone else?

a. Certainly. **b.** Perhaps. **c.** No.

16 Is your family life happy?

a. Usually. **b.** Seldom. **c.** Sometimes.

17 Do you worry about old age?

a. Often. **b.** Sometimes. **c.** Seldom.

18 Could you be poor but happy?

a. Unsure. **b.** No. **c.** Yes.

19 Do you enjoy making plans for the future?

a. Often. **b.** Seldom. **c.** Sometimes.

20 Do you bounce back from misfortune?

a. Easily. **b.** Reasonably well. **c.** With difficulty.

21 Do you regard yourself as a happy person?

a. Usually. **b.** Seldom. **c.** Sometimes.

22 Would you like to change your job?

a. Yes. **b.** Perhaps. **c.** No.

23 Do you have many regrets about the way your life has gone?

a. Some. **b.** Few. **c.** Many.

24. Do you sleep well?

a. Usually. **b.** Sometimes. **c.** Seldom.

score

25. Do you generally enjoy good health?

a. No. **b.** In between. **c.** Yes.

Scoring

For each answer score the number of points indicated.

1.	a:3, b:2, c:1	8.	a:2, b:3, c:1	15.	a:1, b:2, c:3	22.	a:1, b:2, c:3
2.	a:1, b:2, c:3	9.	a:3, b:2, c:1	16.	a:3, b:1, c:2	23.	a:2, b:3, c:1
3.	a:3, b:2, c:1	10.	a:1, b:2, c:3	17.	a:1, b:2, c:3	24.	a:3, b:2, c:1
4.	a:1, b:3, c:2	11.	a:2, b:1, c:3	18.	a:2, b:1, c:3	25.	a:1, b:2, c:3
5.	a:2, b:1, c:3	12.	a:3, b:2, c:1	19.	a:3, b:1, c:2		
6.	a:1, b:3, c:2	13.	a:1, b:3, c:2	20.	a:3, b:2, c:1		
7.	a:3, b:2, c:1	14.	a:1, b:2, c:3	21.	a:3, b:1, c:2		

Over 65

Maximum score is 75. If you scored over 65, you really seem to have little to worry about. You are one of those people for whom life is just a sunny day, and the rest of us can but envy you.

55–64

If you scored between 55 and 64, you are still pretty satisfied with life, and there are very few clouds in your sky. You have occasional worries, but by and large you know how to deal with them.

45–54

With a score of between 45 and 54, you are capable of enjoying happiness, but your life has a few rocky patches that make it hard for you to be as happy as you would like.

35–44

If you scored between 35 and 44, you are really quite beset by troubles and seem to have difficulty in finding real happiness.

30–34

A score from 30 to 34 indicates that you have real problems and don't find much joy in your life at all. At this level of unhappiness you might well consider some sort of counselling to help you.

Below 30

If you scored below 30, then you really are suffering. Your life seems bleak and joyless in the extreme, this could be due to a medically treatable condition. Consider seeing your doctor.

Are you healthy?

This test looks at two related issues. The first is your actual state of health. It includes quite detailed questions about your fitness, diseases you suffer from, hereditary illness in your family, and other similar issues. It is also designed to ascertain your attitude to your health. Do you really care how healthy you are? Do you do things intended to make you healthier? Or are you one of those people who regards worrying about health as a waste of time? Do you eat what you like, drink what you like and, as for going to the gym, forget it? The following questions should test you thoroughly without taxing your strength.

score

1 How many times a week do you take exercise? ☐

    a. Several.   **b.** Once or twice.   **c.** None.

2 Do you play sport? ☐

    a. Never.   **b.** Frequently.   **c.** Sometimes.

3 Do you do cardiovascular exercise (e.g., aerobics, jogging)? ☐

    a. Often.   **b.** Never.   **c.** Sometimes.

4 Do you have your cholesterol level checked? ☐

    a. Occasionally.   **b.** Regularly.   **c.** Never.

5 Do you have your blood pressure checked? ☐

    a. Never.   **b.** Occasionally.   **c.** Regularly.

6 Is your blood pressure normal? ☐

    a. Yes.   **b.** High.   **c.** Low.

7 Do you deliberately try to relax? ☐

    a. Often.   **b.** Sometimes.   **c.** Never.

8 Do you have medical check-ups? ☐

    a. Sometimes.   **b.** Regularly.   **c.** Never.

9 Are you the correct weight for your height? ☐

    a. Overweight.   **b.** Correct weight.   **c.** Underweight.

10 Do you overeat?

a. Never.   **b.** Sometimes.   **c.** Often.

11 Do you drink too much alcohol for the good of your health?

a. Sometimes.   **b.** Often.   **c.** Never.

12 Do you smoke?

a. Never.   **b.** Sometimes.   **c.** Regularly.

13 Could you run for five minutes without getting seriously out of breath?

a. Certainly.   **b.** Probably.   **c.** No.

14 Do you sleep well?

a. Never.   **b.** Sometimes.   **c.** Always.

15 Are you stressed at work?

a. Not at all.   **b.** Very.   **c.** Reasonably.

16 Do you consult the doctor if you notice anything amiss?

a. Never.   **b.** Always.   **c.** Sometimes.

17 Have there been many cases of heart disease in your family?

a. Yes.   **b.** No.   **c.** One or two.

18 Have there been many cases of cancer in your family?

a. No.   **b.** One or two.   **c.** Yes.

19 Are your relatives generally long-lived?

a. Average.   **b.** Yes.   **c.** No.

20 Do you expect to live to a ripe old age?

a. Yes.   **b.** Unsure.   **c.** No.

21 Do you do any form of mental training such as meditation?

a. Never.   **b.** Always.   **c.** Sometimes.

22 Would you regard yourself as healthy?

a. Unsure.   **b.** Yes.   **c.** No.

23 Would you regard yourself as physically fit?

a. Yes.   **b.** No.   **c.** Fairly fit.

24 Do you think your body is supple (considering your age)?

a. Not supple.   **b.** Quite supple.   **c.** Very supple.

25 Have you had any major illnesses in the past 10 years?

a. None.   **b.** Only one.   **c.** More than one.

26 Is there any history of mental illness in your family?

a. Quite a lot.   **b.** None.   **c.** A little.

27 Have you suffered from any psychiatric condition?

a. Never.   b. Persistently.   c. Occasionally.

28 Have you ever suffered from asthma, eczema or hay fever?

a. No.   b. Yes.   c. All three.

29 Do you suffer from any chronic conditions (e.g., diabetes)?

a. None.   b. More than one.   c. One.

30 Have you been hospitalized in the last 10 years?

a. Never.   b. More than once.   c. Once.

31 Do you have your eyes checked regularly?

a. Yes.   b. When I remember.   c. No.

32 Do you have your hearing checked?

a. When I remember.   b. Regularly.   c. Never.

33 Do you have your teeth checked regularly?

a. Yes.   b. When I remember.   c. No.

34 Do you ever check your pulse?

a. No.   b. Yes.   c. Very occasionally.

35 Could you, with sufficient training, complete a 10-mile run?

a. Easily.　　　**b.** With difficulty.　　　**c.** Never.

36 Do you walk rather than take an escalator?

a. Never.　　　**b.** Occasionally.　　　**c.** Always.

37 Do you find talk of healthy living irritating?

a. No.　　　**b.** Yes.　　　**c.** Sometimes.

38 Do you count calories?

a. Never.　　　**b.** Always.　　　**c.** Sometimes.

39 Do you worry about how much fat you consume?

a. Always.　　　**b.** Never.　　　**c.** Sometimes.

40 Do you make a point of eating fresh fruit and vegetables?

a. Sometimes.　　　**b.** Often.　　　**c.** Never.

41 Do you make a point of eating high-fiber foods?

a. Never.　　　**b.** Sometimes.　　　**c.** Often.

42 Do you eat things you like even if they're bad for you?

a. Sometimes.　　　**b.** Never.　　　**c.** Always.

43 Do you read magazine and newspaper articles about health?

a. Often.　　　**b.** Occasionally.　　　**c.** Never.

44 When there is a new public health scare, do you take it seriously?

score ☐

a. Sometimes.   **b.** Never.   **c.** Always.

---

45 Do you worry about catching a serious disease?

score ☐

a. Often.   b. Never.   c. Sometimes.

---

46 Has the occurrence of AIDS made any difference to your sexual habits?

☐

a. None.   **b.** Some.   **c.** A lot.

---

47 Would you have sex with someone you had only just met?

☐

a. Probably.   **b.** Possibly.   **c.** No.

---

48 Do you always wash your hands before eating?

☐

a. Always.   **b.** Never.   **c.** Sometimes.

---

49 Do you tend to ignore minor medical problems and expect them to go away?

☐

a. Sometimes.   **b.** Always.   **c.** Never.

---

50 Do you take your doctor's advice?

☐

a. Never.   **b.** Sometimes.   **c.** Always.

Scoring

For each answer score the number of points indicated.

1.	a:3, b:2, c:1	14.	a:1, b:2, c:3	27.	a:3, b:1, c:2	40.	a:2, b:3, c:1
2.	a:1, b:3, c:2	15.	a:3, b:1, c:2	28.	a:3, b:2, c:1	41.	a:1, b:2, c:3
3.	a:3. b:1, c:2	16.	a:1, b:3, c:2	29.	a:3, b:1, c:2	42.	a:2, b:3, c:1
4.	a:2, b:3, c:1	17.	a:1, b:3, c:2	30.	a:3, b:1, c:2	43.	a:3, b:2, c:1
5.	a:1, b:2, c:3	18.	a:3, b:2, c:1	31.	a:3, b:2, c:1	44.	a:2, b:1, c:3
6.	a:3, b:1, c:2	19.	a:2, b:3, c:1	32.	a:2, b:3, c:1	45.	a:3, b:1, c:2
7.	a:3, b:2, c:1	20.	a:3, b:2, c:1	33.	a:3, b:2, c:1	46.	a:1, b:2, c:3
8.	a:2, b:3, c:1	21.	a:1, b:3, c:2	34.	a:1, b:3, c:2	47.	a:1, b:2, c:3
9.	a:1, b:3, c:2	22.	a:2, b:3, c:1	35.	a:3, b:2, c:1	48.	a:3, b:1, c:2
10.	a:3, b:2, c:1	23.	a:3, b:1, c:2	36.	a:1, b:2, c:3	49.	a:2, b:1, c:3
11.	a:2, b:1, c:3	24.	a:1, b:2, c:3	37.	a:3, b:1, c:2	50.	a:1, b:2, c:3
12.	a:3, b:2, c:1	25.	a:3, b:2, c:1	38.	a:1, b:3, c:2		
13.	a:3, b:2, c:1	26.	a:1, b:3, c:2	39.	a:3, b:1, c:2		

Over 125

Maximum score is 150. If you scored over 125, you are likely to be a very healthy person indeed. You not only enjoy good health now, but you are actively seeking to stay that way. Others may find your concern a little excessive, but you don't care. Just keep on jogging and counting the calories and you could have the last laugh.

110–124

If you scored between 110 and 124, you are not fanatical, but you still find health important and think about it a lot. You take care of yourself and intend to do everything you can to stay healthy. Maybe, from time to time, you relax a bit in your efforts, but this probably does you no harm.

95–109

If you scored between 95 and 109, you are quite healthy and devote some thought to keeping fit, but you don't really work at it. You're probably one of those people who's full of good intentions that you don't pursue.

80–94

With a score between 80 and 94 you don't pay enough attention to your health. You really could improve your situation with a little effort, but you don't seem to care enough to bother.

65–79

If you scored somewhere between 65 and 79, you are quite unhealthy, and your lifestyle does nothing to improve matters.

Below 65

If you scored below 65, you really do have a problem. You simply don't care about good health and seem to have given up on yourself completely. Even in this state you could improve things if you were to get some advice and put a bit of effort into corrective measures.

Are you practical?

Some people seem able to cope with just about any eventuality. Left alone on a desert island they would build a house, catch their own food, and probably find a way of attracting rescuers. Others would simply huddle under a palm tree and hope for the best. Where do you come on this scale? The following questions are designed to sort out the practical, 'I can turn my hand to anything' types from the hopelessly helpless. In these days of sexual equality I have deliberately made no distinction between tasks more usually carried out by one sex or another. My position is that to be regarded as really practical today, you should be able to build a brick wall or bake a cake with equal ease.

score

1 Can you do woodwork repairs?

a. Easily.　　　**b.** With difficulty.　　　**c.** Couldn't cope.

2 Can you repair a window?

a. Easily.　　　**b.** With difficulty.　　　**c.** Couldn't cope.

3 Can you look after children?

a. Easily.　　　**b.** With difficulty.　　　**c.** Couldn't cope.

4 Are you a good gardener?

a. Yes.　　　**b.** Not bad.　　　**c.** No.

5 Can you mend a fuse?

a. Easily.　　　**b.** With difficulty.　　　**c.** Couldn't cope.

6 Can you organize an office?

a. Easily.　　　**b.** With difficulty.　　　**c.** Couldn't cope.

7 Can you repair a car?

a. Easily.　　　**b.** With difficulty.　　　**c.** Couldn't cope.

8 Can you replace a faucet washer?

a. Easily.　　　**b.** With difficulty.　　　**c.** Couldn't cope.

9 Can you provide first aid?

a. Easily.　　　**b.** With difficulty.　　　**c.** Couldn't cope.

score

10 Can you remove a bee sting?

a. Easily.   b. With difficulty.   c. Couldn't cope.

11 Can you decorate a room?

a. Easily.   b. With difficulty.   c. Couldn't cope.

12 Can you change a flat tire?

a. Easily.   b. With difficulty.   c. Couldn't cope.

13 Can you wash clothes?

a. Easily.   b. With difficulty.   c. Couldn't cope.

14 Can you cook a three-course meal?

a. Easily.   b. With difficulty.   c. Couldn't cope.

15 Can you decorate a Christmas tree?

a. Easily.   b. With difficulty.   c. Couldn't cope.

16 Can you lay a patio?

a. Easily.   b. With difficulty.   c. Couldn't cope.

17 Can you pilot a plane?

a. Easily.   b. With difficulty.   c. Couldn't cope.

18 Can you French-polish a table?

a. Easily.   b. With difficulty.   c. Couldn't cope.

19 Can you grow vegetables successfully?

a. Easily.   **b.** With difficulty.   **c.** Couldn't cope.

20 Can you knit?

a. Easily.   **b.** With difficulty.   **c.** Couldn't cope.

21 Can you repair a computer?

a. Easily.   **b.** With difficulty.   **c.** Couldn't cope.

22 Can you drive a large van?

a. Easily.   **b.** With difficulty.   **c.** Couldn't cope.

23 Can you solve crossword puzzles?

a. Easily.   **b.** With difficulty.   **c.** Couldn't cope.

24 Can you understand the layout of a central heating system?

a. Easily.   **b.** With difficulty.   **c.** Couldn't cope.

25 Can you operate a video recorder?

a. Easily.   **b.** With difficulty.   **c.** Couldn't cope.

26 Can you dance a tango?

a. Easily.   **b.** With difficulty.   **c.** Couldn't cope.

27 Can you drive a car?

a. Easily.   **b.** With difficulty.   **c.** Couldn't cope.

score

28 Can you mend broken toys?

a. Easily.   b. With difficulty.   c. Couldn't cope.

29 Can you darn a sock?

a. Easily.   b. With difficulty.   c. Couldn't cope.

30 Can you climb ladders?

a. Easily.   b. With difficulty.   c. Couldn't cope.

31 Can you replace a flat battery on a car?

a. Easily.   b. With difficulty.   c. Couldn't cope.

32 Can you ride a bicycle?

a. Easily.   b. With difficulty.   c. Couldn't cope.

33 Can you water ski?

a. Easily.   b. With difficulty.   c. Couldn't cope.

34 Can you ride a horse?

a. Easily.   b. With difficulty.   c. Couldn't cope.

35 Can you play a sport up to club standard?

a. Easily.   b. With difficulty.   c. Couldn't cope.

36 Can you fill in your tax return without a mistake?

a. Easily.   b. With difficulty.   c. Couldn't cope.

37 Can you climb a tall tree?

score [ ]

a. Easily.   b. With difficulty.   c. Couldn't cope.

38 Can you repair defective gutters?

[ ]

a. Easily.   b. With difficulty.   c. Couldn't cope.

39 Can you build a brick wall?

[ ]

a. Easily.   b. With difficulty.   c. Couldn't cope.

40 Can you repair a broken vase?

[ ]

a. Easily.   b. With difficulty.   c. Couldn't cope.

41 Can you understand the electrical circuitry of your house?

[ ]

a. Easily.   b. With difficulty.   c. Couldn't cope.

42 Can you ride a motor cycle?

[ ]

a. Easily.   b. With difficulty.   c. Couldn't cope.

43 Can you erect a shelf?

[ ]

a. Easily.   b. With difficulty.   c. Couldn't cope.

44 Can you paint a house to a professional standard?

[ ]

a. Easily.   b. With difficulty.   c. Couldn't cope.

45 Can you a lay a concrete path?

[ ]

a. Easily.   b. With difficulty.   c. Couldn't cope.

46 Can you replace a broken roof tile?

a. Easily.   b. With difficulty.   c. Couldn't cope.

47 Can you iron clothes?

a. Easily.   b. With difficulty.   c. Couldn't cope.

48 Can you lay a carpet expertly?

a. Easily.   b. With difficulty.   c. Couldn't cope.

49 Can you lay a lawn using grass seed?

a. Easily.   b. With difficulty.   c. Couldn't cope.

50 Can you speak a second language?

a. Fluently.   b. To school standard.   c. Not at all.

Scoring

(a) answer give yourself 3 points, for every

(b) answer give yourself 2 points, and for every

(c) answer give yourself 1 point.

Over 125

The maximum score is 150. This is a really tough test and to get a high score you would have to be multi-talented. Anything over 125 is really impressive. You're the sort of person who will cope in just about any circumstances. You are practical, capable and indispensable. I'm jealous!

100–124

Between 100 and 124 you are still quite a practical person and are likely to be able to turn your hand to many important tasks. However, there are some things that are beyond you. At least this makes you human.

75–99

Between 75 and 99 you are only average at practical matters, and although you are by no means helpless, you will often have to seek professional advice.

60–74

If you scored between 60 and 74, you are obviously not very practical. Although you can turn your hand to a few tasks, you generally prefer to rely on others to do these things for you.

Below 60

If your score was below 60, you are really not cut out for practical tasks at all. In fact, you must be extremely popular with all the tradesmen in your locality as you are the sort of person who keeps them in work.

Are you thrifty?

People's attitudes to money vary enormously. Some of us let it run right through our fingers while others spend rather carefully. What about you? Do you reach the end of the month with cash to spare, or are you always on the run from the bank manager? Do you give generously, or is getting money from you like squeezing blood from a stone? This test will find out.

score

1 Do you darn socks (or get your partner to do so)?

a. Sometimes. **b.** Often. **c.** Never.

2 About how much do you spend on new clothes each year?

a. $1,500+ **b.** $750+ **c.** $200+

3 How often do you have your car serviced?

a. Every three months
b. Every six months.
c. Only when something goes wrong.

4 Do you:

a. Buy a car and run it till it falls to bits.
b. Change your car fairly regularly.
c. Change your car every year without fail.

5 Regarding your house, do you:

a. Inspect your home regularly to see if anything needs repairing.
b. Only fix things that are actually broken.
c. Keep a casual watch on the state of repairs.

6 Do you save scraps of soap and stick them onto each new block that you buy?

a. Never. **b.** Sometimes. **c.** Always.

7 Do you ever buy clothes, etc. from thrift shops?

a. Often. **b.** Never. **c.** Sometimes.

score

8 Do you buy your cars second-hand?

a. Always. b. Sometimes. c. Never.

9 Do you cook with leftovers?

a. Seldom. b. Never. c. Frequently.

10 Do you pass on children's clothes from older to younger?

a. Often. b. Sometimes. c. Never.

11 Would you ever travel first class?

a. Never. b. Occasionally. c. Often.

12 Would you go to an expensive restaurant for a celebration?

a. Occasionally. b. Always. c. Never.

13 Do you buy designer label clothes?

a. Never. b. Seldom. c. Frequently.

14 Would you pay $100 per head in a restaurant?

a. Possibly. b. Probably. c. Absolutely not.

15 Do you sort out your rubbish for recycling?

a. Of course. b. Never think about it. c. When I remember.

16 Do you make useful things from bits of rubbish?

a. Often.   **b.** Seldom   **c.** Never.

17 Do you make a habit of choosing supermarket 'own brands.'

a. Never.   **b.** Often.   **c.** Sometimes.

18 Do you improve cheap food with spices and flavorings?

a. Sometimes.   **c.** Always.   **b.** Never.

19 Do you prefer dried flowers because they last longer?

a. Certainly.   **b.** Not really.   **c.** No.

20 Would you eat something you didn't like just because it was cheap?

a. Probably.   **b.** No.   **c.** Possibly.

21 Would you let your children wear shabby clothes if it saved you money?

a. No.   **b.** Of course.   **c.** Maybe.

22 Do you go on foreign holidays?

a. You must be joking.   **b.** Frequently.   **c.** When I can afford it.

23

How often do you eat out?

a. Every week.   **b.** Once a month.   **c.** On special occasions only.

24

How often do you go to the movies?

a. Every week.   **b.** Once a month.   **c.** Once in a blue moon.

25

Do you get real pleasure from saving money?

a. No.   **b.** A little.   **c.** Yes.

Scoring

For each answer score the number of points indicated.

1.	a:2, b:3, c:1	**8.**	a:3, b:2, c:1	**15.**	a:3, b:1, c:2	**22.**	a:3, b:1, c:2
2.	a:1, b:2, c:3	**9.**	a:2, b:1, c:3	**16.**	a:3, b:2, c:1	**23.**	a:1, b:2, c:3
3.	a:1, b:2, c:3	**10.**	a:3, b:2, c:1	**17.**	a:1, b:3, c:2	**24.**	a:1, b:2, c:3
4.	a:3, b:2, c:1	**11.**	a:3, b:2, c:1	**18.**	a:2, b:3, c:1	**25.**	a:1, b:2, c:3
5.	a:1, b:3, c:2	**12.**	a:2, b:1, c:3	**19.**	a:3, b:2, c:1		
6.	a:1, b:2, c:3	**13.**	a:3, b:2, c:1	**20.**	a:3, b:1, c:2		
7.	a:3, b:1, c:2	**14.**	a:2, b:1, c:3	**21.**	a:1, b:3, c:2		

Maximum score is 75. If you scored **70 or more**, you are so mean that Scrooge would despise you. How can you live with yourself?

If you scored between **60 and 69**, you are pretty tight-fisted but probably think of yourself as 'careful.' You actually suffer from short arms and deep pockets.

A score of **40 to 59** would suggest that you are quite sensible about money but not exactly mean. You would think twice before splashing out, but in the right mood you know how to enjoy yourself.

A score of **30 to 39** suggests that you don't care too much for economizing and like to enjoy what you earn without much thought for tomorrow.

If you scored **below 30**, enjoy it while you've still got it (which won't be long.)

Are you assertive?

It's hard to get ahead in highly competitive areas without being pushy. Putting yourself forward is important in the rat race. So let's test just how assertive you can be.

If someone pushes into line ahead of you, do you:

a) Harangue him in embarrassingly loud tones until he gives up.

b) Say, "Erm, sorry but I was here first."

c) Suffer in silence.

If you get poor service in a shop, do you:

a) Go home and write to the CEO of the company setting out your grievance in full.

b) Shout at the shop assistant.

c) Make bitter remarks to your fellow shoppers but fail to complain to the staff.

You take something to be mended and when you get it home the fault hasn't been fixed. Do you:

a) Phone the repair place and explain the problem.

b) Try to fix it yourself.

c) Storm back to the repair shop and demand to see the manager.

Whilst browsing in a bookshop you notice someone else's book full of your plagiarized ideas. Do you:

a) Take no notice, it might just be coincidence.

b) Consult a lawyer.

c) Contact the author to seek an explanation.

You try to attract attention in a crowded shop but don't get noticed. Do you:

a) Storm out in disgust.

b) Wait patiently until you get served.

c) Make a fuss until someone gives you attention.

You go for a job interview. Do you:

a) Explain confidently why you are the best person for the job.

b) Describe your qualifications and hope for the best.

c) Look at all the other candidates in the waiting room and wish you hadn't bothered.

7 Your child comes home and complains of having been picked on by her teacher. Do you:
a) Tell her to take no notice, it will all pass over.
b) Ask for an appointment with the teacher to sort the matter out.
c) Tell your child she has to stand up for herself.

8 Your neighbour regularly plays loud music late at night. Do you:
a) Call the police.
b) Go round and complain.
c) Improve your sound insulation.

9 You get overlooked for promotion. Do you:
a) Resign.
b) Complain to the boss that you deserved better.
c) Work hard to do better next time.

10 You need a raise. Do you:
a) Go straight to the boss and ask for one.
b) Take on extra work and hope that you get noticed.
c) Make some economies in your life style.

11 You feel your boss does not appreciate your contribution to the company. Do you:
a) Complain to your colleagues and hope he gets to hear about it.
b) Ask for a staff review.
c) Look through the 'situations vacant' ads.

12 At a public meeting you find yourself in complete disagreement with the speaker. Do you:
a) Leave the meeting.
b) Whisper your objections to the friend sitting beside you.
c) Stand up and ask pointed questions.

13 Members of a religious sect with which you disagree come to your door. Do you:
a) Tell them to go away.
b) Invite them in and set out your objections at length.
c) Make a financial contribution to get rid of them.

14 Someone comes around collecting for charity. You already support a number of charities and cannot really afford to give more. Do you:

a) Say that you're sorry but you have no change right now.

b) Explain honestly that you think you give enough.

c) Ignore the door bell and let them think you're out.

15 A political candidate comes to your door canvassing support in a forthcoming election. Do you:

a) Tell him frankly that you won't be voting for him.

b) Say that you will vote for him (you have also said this to all the other candidates).

c) Discuss the issues and say that you will make up your mind later.

16 Friends invite you to join them at a play you suspect will be boring. Do you:

a) Go anyway and do your best to take an interest.

b) Point out that it's going to be dull and suggest doing something else.

c) Phone up at the last minute and say you're ill.

17 A person you find attractive makes some remarks with which you cannot agree. Do you:

a) Say nothing, you don't want to spoil your chances of a relationship.

b) Argue strongly for your own view and hope that honesty wins you Brownie points.

c) Remonstrate mildly but give up before you get into a real argument.

18 Is it more important to state your views clearly than to be popular?

a) Yes.

b) No.

c) Not sure.

19 A friend asks your opinion of some clothes s/he has just bought. Do you:

a) Say honestly that they were not a good choice.

b) Change the subject.

c) Damn with faint praise and hope that the hint is taken.

		score

Would you keep quiet on a subject you felt strongly about just to keep the peace?

20
a) Probably.
b) Certainly not.
c) Maybe.

Your mother-in-law arrives for the weekend and starts criticizing everything in your home. Do you:

21
a) Tell her that if she doesn't like it she can go straight home.
b) Take no notice, she'll be gone by Monday.
c) Quietly point out that your lifestyle suits you very well.

You find yourself at a sports match among a group of rival supporters. Do you:

22
a) Keep very quiet and hide your team colours.
b) Shout loudly for your team.
c) Joke with the rival supporters about being a member of the opposition.

A very large drunk in a bar is making obnoxious racist comments. Do you:

23
a) Leave the bar before trouble starts.
b) Try to start a discussion about the issues.
c) Tell him loudly that he's a bigot.

You see a police officer parking illegally to go and collect his dry cleaning. Do you:

24
a) Confront him and complain.
b) Ignore it, you don't want trouble with the police.
c) Write to his boss and make an official complaint.

At a PTA meeting you feel strongly that you should voice an unpopular point of view. Do you:

25
a) Say what you feel regardless of who you offend.
b) Keep quiet, you have to live with these people.
c) Write to the PTA Committee after the meeting stating your point of view.

Scoring

The maximum score is 75.

	1	2	3		1	2	3		1	2	3
1	c	b	a	10	c	b	a	19	b	c	a
2	c	b	a	11	c	a	b	20	a	c	b.
3	b	a	c	12	a	b	c	21	b	c	a
4	a	b	c	13	c	a	b	22	a	c	b
5	a	b	c	14	c	a	b	23	a	b	c
6	c	b	a	15	b	c	a	24	b	c	a
7	a	c	b	16	b	c	a	25	b	c	a
8	c	a	b	17	c	a	b				
9	a	c	b	18	a	c	b				

70–75

Yes, you're very assertive and will have no trouble getting people to take notice of what you say. It doesn't make you a genius but, if you've got what it takes, then at least you won't be ignored. You probably upset people by being so forthright but, if you want to make it in the genius league, you can't afford to let that kind of thing worry you or change your mind. And you don't.

60–69

You're quite assertive and do not usually have trouble getting your point across. However, to be accepted as a genius you may need to be even more forceful. The genius business is a tough one to break into and you'll need all the assertiveness you can muster.

40–59

No. You're too nice. Either toughen up or forget any dreams of genius. No one is going to take you seriously.

below 40

You're joking, right?

Test **Twenty Eight**

Are you arrogant?

This one is going to be a trifle difficult. It's hard to imagine someone self-effacing making it in the high-flying world. We've already tested assertiveness and that was all right because no one really minds being called assertive. Even 'bossy' is not too bad. But arrogant? Oh dear. Let's see how you get on.

	score
'If you don't like it you can lump it!' Is this something you would say?	
1	
a) No, that's incredibly rude.	
b) Why not? You have to show people where they stand.	
c) I might if I was provoked enough.	

'If you don't like it you can lump it!' Is this something you would say?

1
a) No, that's incredibly rude.
b) Why not? You have to show people where they stand.
c) I might if I was provoked enough.

'The bigger they come the harder they fall.' Do you believe this?

2
a) That's right. Hit 'em hard so they don't get up.
b) Erm, it's usually a case of, 'The bigger they come the harder I fall.'
c) Yes, that's right. In theory at least.

'You don't have to agree with me as long as you do as I say.' Would you agree with this?

3
a) It's sometimes necessary to be forceful.
b) That is just *so* arrogant.
c) Yes, you have to show people where they stand. Or kneel, preferably.

'I always like to listen to the other person's point of view.' Is this a policy you endorse?

4
a) Why?
b) Yes, if I have the time.
c) Of course, I would always do it.

'It is far better to reach a mutually satisfactory agreement than to force someone to admit defeat.' Your reaction?

5
a) Of course, that's the way it should be.
b) If you can make that work, then fine. Otherwise you have to use force.
c) No, you just stamp and shout until you get your own way.

'I'd make a wonderful diplomat.' Would you?

6
a) No, I'd start World War 3.
b) Yes, I'm very good at diplomacy.
c) I'm quite diplomatic.

Do you feel it necessary to consult other people and take notice of their opinions?

7
a) It's often very valuable.
b) Why should I? What do they know?
c) It can be useful sometimes.

Barefaced cheek gets you a long way in life. Do you agree?

8
a) Yes, it seldom fails.
b) I wouldn't know, I've never tried.
c) It's not a tactic I use often, but it has worked occasionally.

'People listen to me because I'm always right.' Agree?

9
a) No, I don't like that at all.
b) No, I'm right sometimes but I wouldn't claim to be infallible.
c) Call me arrogant if you like but that's the way it is.

'I think that a certain amount of modesty is essential for a well-rounded character.' What do you think.

10
a) Who wants to be 'well rounded'? If you've got it flaunt it!
b) I think modesty is very important.
c) Modesty is OK, but you can overdo it.

'When driving I expect others to get out of my way.' Agree?

11
a) I try to play fair with other road users.
b) My time is important, OK? I don't need people slowing me down.
c) Sometimes I'm in a hurry and need to push ahead, but I try not to.

'I'm embarrassed if people defer to me.' Does this seem familiar?

12
a) I'm furious if they don't.
b) Yes, that's what I'm like.
c) I can empathize with that, though I try not to be too self-effacing.

'I expect people to admire my achievements.' Do you?

13
a) No, not really.
b) It would be nice if they recognized my worth.
c) They'll regret it if they don't!

'I am not one of the common herd.' Does that describe you?

14
a) I wouldn't put it quite like that, though I do think I have great ability.
b) Good gracious no!
c) Of course it describes me. Who else?

15 'I have nothing to declare except my genius.' Would you agree with Oscar Wilde?

a) No, of course not.

b) Not really, though I do have great talent.

c) Yes, of course. Who's Oscar Wilde?

16 'My work is of the utmost importance to mankind.' Is yours?

a) Naturally.

b) No, not at all.

c) It's quite important but not vital.

17 'My name will go down in history.' Will yours?

a) No.

b) I would like to think so, but I'm not sure.

c) Of course.

18 'People are unable to understand my true greatness.' Agree?

a) Yes, but the loss is theirs.

b) No, that's rubbish.

c) I'm good but I'm not *that* good.

19 'My family has to revolve around me.' Agree?

a) I usually try to fit in but sometimes my needs have to come first.

b) I always consider others.

c) Yes, just like the Solar System.

20 'I enjoy the limelight.' Do you?

a) Not at all.

b) It's nice for a change.

c) Enjoy? Try 'demand'.

21 'I deserve the admiration and respect of others.' Do you?

a) Yes, I suppose so.

b) No, I wouldn't say that.

c) Yes, and I'd better get it, too.

'There are only a couple of hundred people who really run things in this country, and I'm one of them.' Are you?

22
a) I don't think that's true and, even if it is, it certainly doesn't include me.
b) I'm influential, but not that influential.
c) Yes, that's the way things work.

'People recognize me wherever I go.' Is this you?

23
a) Yes, I'm used to it.
b) Some people know me if they read my work.
c) No, I'm not at all famous.

'When I go anywhere I expect to be treated like a VIP.' Do you?

24
a) No, I'd hate that.
b) Yes, I'd accept nothing less.
c) On some occasions.

'Other people only exist to make my life easier.' Do you agree?

25
a) Of course, a genius has to be pampered.
b) That is just so ugly.
c) Maybe, to some extent.

Scoring

The maximum score is 75.

	1	2	3		1	2	3		1	2	3
1	a	c	b	10	b	c	a	19	b	a	c
2	b	c	a	11	a	c	b	20	a	b	c
3	b	a	c	12	b	c	a	21	b	a	c
4	c	b	a	13	a	b	c	22	a	b	c
5	a	b	c	14	b	a	c	23	c	b	a
6	b	c	a	15	a	b	c	24	a	c	b
7	a	c	b	16	b	c	a	25	b	c	a
8	b	c	a	17	a	b	c				
9	a	b	c	18	b	c	a				

70–75

Your arrogance is such that you won't even be reading this. You know how great you are.

60–69

Genius is within your reach on this score. You are pretty arrogant, but not so bad that you can't see the offence you give.

40–59

You don't really understand arrogance that well. You have too much of a conscience ever to be really arrogant.

below 40

You're far too pleasant for the genius game. Congratulations!

Are you charismatic?

Charisma, is the magnetic power that attracts people to you. It won't affect the quality of your work or provide you with wonderful, original ideas but it remains one of the most vital talents if you want to make it big in life. If people who don't even understand what you're talking about believe that you are in fact a genius, you will have made it. The following test will decide whether you've got what it takes.

Do people find themselves attracted to you?

a)   Yes, it can be embarrassing sometimes.

b)   No, no more than other people.

c)   I suppose they do a bit.

Do you find that people agree with you regardless of the quality of your arguments?

a)   No, never.

b)   Not that often.

c)   All the time.

Would you make a good political leader?

a)   Yes, people would vote for me no matter what my policies were.

b)   No, with the best policies in the world I couldn't get elected.

c)   I'd be average.

Would you find it easy to attract followers?

a)   No, not at all.

b)   Not very easy.

c)   Yes, it's really no problem.

Do you find casual acquaintances open up and tell you their life story in intimate detail?

a)   Occasionally.

b)   Never.

c)   Happens all the time. Sometimes I just can't get away.

Do children and animals take to you immediately?

a)   They usually bite me.

b)   I get on with them OK, I suppose.

c)   Yes, I'm always popular with kids and pets.

Do strangers choose to sit next to you on the train?

a)   Frequently.

b)   Sometimes.

c)   As little as possible.

8   **Do people come up to you in the street and ask directions?**

a)   Not often.

b)   Sometimes.

c)   Very often.

9   **Do you ever feel that people avoid you for no obvious reason?**

a)   Yes, it's unpleasant and I don't understand it.

b)   It has happened very occasionally.

c)   No, that never happens to me.

10   **Does your work attract disciples?**

a)   Yes, frequently.

b)   Not at all.

c)   I suppose a few.

11   **Could you sway a crowd just by force of personality?**

a)   I have done many times.

b)   No, I'd need more than that.

c)   I could influence them a bit, but not make them storm the Bastille, for example.

12   **Do people customarily look to you for leadership?**

a)   From time to time.

b)   Absolutely never.

c)   Very frequently.

13   **Do old friends keep in touch with you even though there is no practical advantage to them?**

a)   Yes, I still have friends from the distant past.

b)   No, gone and forgotten, that's me.

c)   I have some old friends.

14   **Do people tend to fall in love with you?**

a)   No more than usually, I guess.

b)   Yes, it happens all the time. I'm used to it.

c)   No, that isn't really my problem. Worse luck.

15 Do people tend to be possessive over you?

a)   No, never.

b)   Not often.

c)   Yes, it can be a real problem.

16 Do you feel that you have some sort of supernormal power over people?

a)   I might do sometimes.

b)   No, not at all.

c)   Yes, I have suspected it.

17 Could you face down an angry mob?

a)   I'd try but wouldn't guarantee the result.

b)   I'd get lynched.

c)   I could do it.

18 Would people accept an unusual idea just because you proposed it?

a)   Possibly.

b)   No, the fact that it was mine would make things more difficult.

c)   Yes, that would be enough.

19 Do you find it easy to take the lead in public discussions?

a)   Not at all.

b)   Yes, I do it all the time.

c)   Sometimes.

20 Are you good at being a follower?

a)   No, I always lead.

b)   Yes, it suits my personality.

c)   I can be follower or leader according to the situation.

21 Do you get frightened if people make demands of you?

a)   No, I'm used to it.

b)   It disturbs me slightly.

c)   I find it quite alarming.

score

Would you consider a career as a popular entertainer?

a) I'd hate every minute of it.
b) The thought does attract me.
c) I'm not sure. I might like it.

Do you find the attention of others stimulating?

a) Yes, of course.
b) No, it embarrasses me.
c) I'm so used to it I hardly notice any more, but I suppose I would miss it.

Regardless of your actual religious beliefs, do you have the skill to be a preacher?

a) Oh yes, nothing would be easier.
b) I could, but I don't know how successful I'd be.
c) No, I'd have an empty church.

Could you sell things just by the force of your personality?

a) No, not at all.
b) I might do quite well.
c) No problem at all. People always want to please me.

Scoring

The maximum score is 75.

	1	2	3		1	2	3		1	2	3
1	b	c	a	10	b	c	a	19	a	c	b
2	a	b	c	11	b	c	a	20	b	c	a
3	b	c	a	12	b	a	c	21	c	b	a
4	a	b	c	13	b	c	a	22	a	c	b
5	b	a	c	14	c	a	b	23	b	a	c
6	a	b	c	15	a	b	c	24	c	b	a
7	c	b	a	16	b	a	c	25	a	b	c
8	a	b	c	17	b	a	c				
9	a	b	c	18	b	a	c				

70–75

You have massive charisma. Your influence over others, for good or ill, is very strong.

60–69

You are quite charismatic and could easily convince people of your genius. You have a considerable influence.

40–59

People find you likeable. They will listen patiently to your ideas but, in the end, will make up their minds according to the facts.

below 40

Charisma is not really your strong suit, is it?

Test Thirty

Are you a conceptual thinker?

Conceptual thinking involved looking at the big picture, not details.
People generally are better at one or the other. Are you a nuts-and-bolts person or more of a 'blue sky' thinker?

1 **Would you rather understand the principles by which your central heating system works, or be able to fix it when it goes wrong?**

a) I don't really care as long as it works.

b) I would want to understand all about it.

c) I'm happy to be able to fix it, but I don't care about the theory.

2 **Can you repair a car engine?**

a) Wouldn't have a clue!

b) Yes, that's no problem.

c) I'd try, but wouldn't guarantee the result.

3 **Do you toy with ideas just for the fun of it?**

a) Yes, all the time.

b) No, there's no point to it.

c) Yes, some ideas intrigue me.

4 **Do you like to tinker with machinery?**

a) I don't mind.

b) I couldn't be bothered.

c) I'm never happier than when playing with machines.

5 **Are you really into DIY?**

a) Not at all.

b) Only when my partner nags me.

c) Yes, I find it very satisfying.

6 **Do you enjoy mathematics?**

a) Yes, I'm fascinated by it.

b) No, it bores me.

c) I'm quite interested.

7 **Can you understand music theory?**

a) Not at all.

b) Yes, of course.

c) I did a bit at school.

score

8 Do you play chess?

a) Yes, I'm very keen when I get the time.

b) I can play but don't often bother.

c) No, I never mastered it.

9 Would you rather fix a broken machine or go to a concert?

a) I'd quite enjoy either.

b) Give me the machine any day.

c) I'd rather go to the dentist than fix a machine!

10 Do you itch to know how things work?

a) Yes, I'm full of curiosity.

b) No, as long as they work that's fine by me.

c) I'm quite interested but not obsessed.

11 Do you ache to understand why things work?

a) Yes, that's more like it!

b) Yes, that's quite interesting.

c) No, couldn't care less.

12 Would you learn a new language even if you had no chance to use it?

a) What for?

b) I might.

c) Yes, there are all sorts of languages I'd love to learn but none of them is that useful.

13 Would you rather theorize about the universe or help build a space rocket?

a) I'd enjoy both.

b) The rocket sounds fun.

c) I enjoy theorizing.

14 Do your friends regard you as a little impractical?

a) I suppose they do.

b) That's the last thing anyone would say about me.

c) No, I don't think so.

Does everyone turn to you when machines break down?

15
a) Always.
b) Not unless they want them broken a bit more!
c) Mending machines is not what I do best.

Can you programme the video (VCR)?

16
a) Yes, can't everyone?
b) I sometimes get it wrong.
c) The damn thing hates me!

Do you just pay people to sort out the practical aspects of your life?

17
a) I wouldn't have put it quite so bluntly, but yes.
b) There are some things I just can't do myself.
c) No. I'd never need that sort of help.

Do you find philosophy intriguing?

18
a) Not in the slightest.
b) I'm fairly interested.
c) Yes, I'd love to devote more time to it.

Do you see academic research as out of touch with reality?

19
a) Not really.
b) Yes, academics give me a pain.
c) No, of course not. Research is *about* reality.

Do you take pride in your ability to make machines work?

20
a) Yes, I do.
b) No, it would be misplaced pride in my case.
c) Machines are in a conspiracy against me.

Do you take pride in not knowing how machines work?

21
a) Yes, I hate them as much as they hate me.
b) No, I can't stand people like that.
c) No, ignorance is never something to be proud of.

Can you drive a car?

22

a) Yes, I'm an excellent driver.

b) Yes, like most people I guess.

c) No, I've never bothered to learn.

If the written language of the Philistines were discovered tomorrow, would you be excited?

23

a) That would be incredible!

b) Why would I care about some dead Philistines?

c) Interesting, but not that interesting.

Do you think much about the meaning of life?

24

a) Sometimes.

b) No, I'm too busy.

c) Yes, of course, it's the most important question there is.

Would you like to be in charge of, say, the engine room of an aircraft carrier?

25

a) Can you afford to lose the ship?

b) No, not quite me.

c) Yes, just give me the chance!

Scoring

The maximum score is 75.

	1	2	3		1	2	3		1	2	3
1	b	c	a	10	a	c	b	19	b	a	c
2	b	c	a	11	c	b	a	20	a	b	c
3	b	c	a	12	a	b	c	21	b	c	a
4	c	a	b	13	b	a	c	22	a	b	c
5	c	b	a	14	b	c	a	23	b	c	a
6	b	c	a	15	a	c	b	24	b	a	c
7	a	c	b	16	a	b	c	25	c	b	a
8	c	b	a	17	c	b	a				
9	b	a	c	18	a	b	c				

70–75

You are almost entirely conceptual in your thinking. You don't have a practical bone in your body and you don't care. Your life is spent wrestling with abstract concepts which you find completely fascinating and you let others take care of the practicalities. You have definite genius potential as long as you don't trip over your untied shoelaces and break your neck first.

60–69

You are strongly conceptual in your thinking but not entirely unaware of the practicalities of life. You could not only design an experiment but could probably make it work. OK, you could tell someone else how to make it work. Your genius potential is quite high but, if it doesn't work out, your chances of a job in a garage are not good.

40–59

You're far too practical to be a genius. You can mend fuses and, probably, program the video.

below 40

You wouldn't know a concept if you found one in your lunch. By the way, you just got grease marks all over this book!

Are you in control?

To be a genius you need to be fully in control of your life. More than that: you need to believe you are in control. Are you the sort of person who is master of his fate, or do you *believe* that your life is controlled from outside? This test will help you find that out.

Are you fully confident of the course your life is taking?

1.
a) It's taking the course I want, naturally.
b) I worry about it sometimes.
c) I have no idea where my life is going.

Do you feel that you are in the 'driving seat' of your life?

2.
a) No, I think I'm more of a passenger.
b) Yes, I'm mostly in control.
c) Yes, and I don't allow back seat drivers either!

Do you believe in fate?

3.
a) I suppose so.
b) Yes, I believe very strongly that some things are pre-ordained.
c) No, I've no patience with rubbish like that.

Do you make your own luck?

4.
a) No, I think luck comes from elsewhere.
b) Yes, you have to.
c) I try to help myself as best I can.

Would you like to captain an ocean-going liner?

5.
a) I'd be terrified.
b) I'd love the challenge.
c) I'd like to but I'm not sure that I could.

What do you think of the saying, 'You can't fight city hall'?

6.
a) Nonsense, you can fight anyone.
b) It's probably true.
c) You can always fight, but you may not win.

Do you wear the pants in your family?

7.
a) No, my partner does.
b) We all get along just fine without power games.
c) Yes, of course.

What are you like as a subordinate?

8
a) Dreadful, I always know best.
b) I don't mind taking orders at all.
c) I'm OK but I sometimes question decisions.

Do you like team games?

9
a) Yes, I enjoy the camaraderie.
b) I don't mind, but I'm not that keen.
c) Only if I get to be captain.

Do you fear responsibility?

10
a) A bit.
b) It can be quite frightening to be in charge.
c) I need the feeling of being in control.

Do you tend to blame society for juvenile delinquency?

11
a) To a certain extent.
b) Yes, I think young people are led astray by society's lack of values.
c) People are responsible for themselves. No one makes you become a criminal.

Would you like to be self-employed?

12
a) No, it would be too risky.
b) I wouldn't mind, but it would be scary.
c) I couldn't work any other way.

Would you like to be part of a community, like the army, for example?

13
a) Yes, I like the thought of other people taking some of the responsibility.
b) No, I can't stand all that 'team spirit' stuff.
c) I wouldn't mind too much

14. Do you think people should have total responsibility for their own lives?

a) That seems rather harsh to me.

b) Maybe, but a little help is sometimes needed.

c) Yes, how could you live any other way?

15. Do you hate giving up control when you are ill?

a) It drives me mad.

b) No, I quite enjoy the rest from responsibility.

c) I don't mind letting go for a while.

16. Do you sometimes feel that life is against you?

a) Not really.

b) Yes, I often feel that way.

c) Couldn't care less, I'm in charge of my life.

17. Do you believe we have free will?

a) I'm not sure.

b) No I don't think we do.

c) I know I do.

18. Do you ever read your horoscope?

a) Yes, just for fun.

b) I take it quite seriously.

c) What a load of rubbish!

19. Is the course of your life pre-determined?

a) Of course not.

b) It might be.

c) Yes, I think there are things we cannot change.

20. Do you ever feel in need of divine help?

a) All the time.

b) I believe God does help us.

c) No, I can make it on my own, thank you.

Do you have complete faith in yourself?

21

a) Yes, who else should I have it in?

b) Mostly.

c) No, quite often I doubt myself.

Are you certain that you are in control of your life?

22

a) Quite certain.

b) I like to think so.

c) I'm not at all sure.

Do you have faith in the power of the Government to control your life?

23

a) What, a crowd of sleazy politicians? I certainly don't need *them*.

b) Yes, of course, after all we elected them.

c) On the whole I'm happy to let them be in control.

Do you always know best?

24

a) About my own life, certainly.

b) I'm open to advice.

c) I often need someone to tell me what to do.

Are you the captain of your ship?

25

a) Yes, and I don't stand for any mutinies either!

b) Most of the time.

c) No, someone else seems to run my ship

Scoring

The maximum score is 75.

	1	2	3		1	2	3		1	2	3
1	c	b	a	10	b	a	c	19	c	b	a
2	a	b	c	11	b	a	c	20	a	b	c
3	b	a	c	12	a	b	c	21	c	b	a
4	a	c	b	13	a	c	b	22	c	b	a
5	a	c	b	14	a	b	c	23	b	c	a
6	b	c	a	15	b	c	a	24	c	b	a
7	a	b	c	16	b	a	c	25	c	b	a
8	b	c	a	17	b	a	c				
9	a	b	c	18	b	a	c				

70–75

You are very self-directed and this will stand you in good stead in your quest to become a genius. Other people may find you rather distant and a bit bossy but, on the other hand, there will be plenty of time when they are grateful to you for taking charge. Either way you won't care much, you'll just get on with knowing best.

60–69

You are quite firmly in charge of your own life. You have no truck with luck, fate, or the Government when it comes to knowing what is best for you. But you are aware that you can't always be in charge however much you might want to be.

40–59

You don't really understand about being in control of your life. You are far too dependent on outside help to ever make it in the genius league.

below 40

Your life appears to be controlled from another planet. Possibly another galaxy

Can you defer gratification?

What exactly is 'deferred gratification?', you might well ask. OK, imagine you're a toddler and someone says to you, "I'll give you a marshmallow. You can eat it right away if you want. But in a moment I'm going to leave the room and if, when I come back, you *haven't* eaten your marshmallow, I'll give you two more." What would you do? Why does it matter? Well, a psychologist tried this experiment with some kids and got an interesting result. Kids who showed they were capable of deferred gratification – ie, those who could wait in order to gain an advantage – did much better in later life than those who ate the marshmallow straight away. So a capacity for deferred gratification can be highly desirable. Can you do it? Try this test to find out.

<table>
<tr><td></td><td>score</td></tr>
</table>

1 **Let's start with the marshmallow. Could you wait, say, 20 minutes in order to get two more marshmallows? Be honest!**

a) Yes, I could wait twice that long if I had to.

b) No, I'd give in and eat the one in my hand.

c) I'd probably be able to wait but it would be a very close thing.

2 **Do you sneak a look at presents?**

a) I have done.

b) No, that would spoil the surprise.

c) I always do, I just can't help it.

3 **Do you often say, 'I can't *wait*!' and actually mean it?**

a) Never.

b) Oh, yes!

c) Not often, but sometimes.

4 **Would you plant a tree that was slow growing, an oak, say?**

a) I might do.

b) Of course, it would be my gift to the future.

c) Why? What would be the point?

5 **Would you save up for an expensive holiday that you couldn't go on for five years, or would you rather go on cheaper holidays now?**

a) I'd take the cheaper holidays. Who knows how long you're going to live?

b) I would consider saving up.

c) I'd definitely save.

6 **Do you sneak food from the kitchen when a meal is being prepared?**

a) No, I've never done such a thing.

b) Yes, sometimes I can't resist.

c) Of course, doesn't everyone?

Does waiting for something good to happen frustrate you?

7
a) No, I rather enjoy the anticipation.
b) I scream with frustration.
c) I don't mind too much, as long as I don't wait long.

You finish a good book and want to get the sequel from the library. Someone's got it out on loan. What do you do?

8
a) Rush to the book store and buy a copy.
b) Reserve the book and wait until it comes back into circulation.
c) Wait with growing impatience.

You want to buy some new clothes. The shop you normally go to is out of stock but will have what you want by next week. Their other branch, 50 miles away, has just what you want right now. Do you:

9
a) Wait until your local branch has what you want.
b) Jump in the car and drive the 50 miles.
c) Call the other branch to see if they will let you order by phone.

Do you find waiting for something you want comes easily to you?

10
a) To be honest it doesn't come to me at all.
b) I don't mind waiting a bit.
c) I never mind waiting, the result is usually worth it.

You're waiting to see the latest movie. There's an announcement that the projector has broken down and it will take half an hour to get it fixed. Do you:

11
a) Go out and get a pizza, then come back in half an hour.
b) Wait uncomplainingly for the fault to be fixed.
c) Complain strongly to the manager, then spend the half hour in a filthy temper.

You or your partner is expecting a baby. You *could* find out what sex it is going to be. Do you?

12
a) Yes, I couldn't bear not to know.
b) I might, depending on what my partner wanted.
c) I would wait. Knowing would spoil the surprise, wouldn't it?

290

13   **You take an exam but then go on holiday abroad. The results will be sent to you by mail. Eventually. Do you:**

a) Hang around foreign post offices waiting for a message.

b) Make a very expensive phone call to find out.

c) Wait until you get back to find out.

14   **You're sent away on business which involves you being separated from your partner/lover. What do you do?**

a) Get the job done as quickly as possible and go home.

b) Phone, write, email, rush through the job and catch the first flight back.

c) Take your time and do the work thoroughly. A break will do you both good.

15   **How long could you wait for something you *really* wanted?**

a) Given a choice, seconds.

b) Certainly hours or days, weeks or months would be a problem.

c) Years, if necessary.

16   **Do you think that patience is a virtue?**

a) Yes, and one that I possess.

b) No, but I'm quite patient.

c) No, I hate patience. Why should I be patient?!

17   **Do you have a pension?**

a) What for? I mean, I'm not going to retire for years.

b) Of course, it is better to be prudent.

c) Yes, though I don't pay as much into it as I should.

18   **Would you devote yourself to a long-term project, such as scientific research, that might not pay off for many years, if at all?**

a) I might if the work was sufficiently interesting.

b) Life's too short.

c) I certainly would. Anything worth doing takes time.

19

A mysterious present arrives unexpectedly. However, you have an urgent appointment to attend. What do you do?

a) Rip the paper off, open the present and forget about the appointment.

b) Leave the tempting parcel until you get back. Anticipation is half the pleasure.

c) Go to the appointment and get away as quickly as possible to get to your surprise.

20

You are offered a new job with more pay. However, if you stay where you are your prospects within three years are excellent. What do you do?

a) Go, you've had enough of this place anyway.

b) Stay, the rewards of patience may be rich.

c) Hang on a bit longer, but still look out for other offers.

21

'Everything comes to he who waits' Agree?

a) I suppose quite often that's true.

b) I think that is only common sense.

c) No. You have to go out and grab what you want.

22

Could you work in a job where promotion is by the 'dead men's shoes' method?

a) Yes, it wouldn't bother me.

b) If I did, some people would be dead sooner than expected!

c) I suppose I could, but I'd get very frustrated.

23

At the end of next week you're going to be given a huge honour which will be televised nationally. How do you feel?

a) Can't wait!

b) It'll be nice when it happens.

c) A bit nervous but otherwise OK.

24

You want to go to a sports match but first you need to do some household chores. Do you:

a) Forget the chores and slide out of the house unnoticed.

b) Do your chores conscientiously.

c) Rush to get the work done so that you can get away sooner.

You stand to inherit a lot of money from a distant relative. Do you:

b) Think about it sometimes with longing.

c) Wish ardently that the relative would go to his reward.
   After all, it's not as if he's anyone close...

score

Scoring

The maximum score is 75.

	1	2	3		1	2	3		1	2	3
1	b	c	a	10	a	b	c	19	a	c	b
2	c	a	b	11	c	a	b	20	a	c	b
3	b	c	a	12	a	b	c	21	c	a	b
4	c	a	b	13	b	a	c	22	b	c	a
5	a	b	c	14	b	a	c	23	a	c	b
6	c	b	a	15	a	b	c	24	a	c	b
7	b	c	a	16	c	b	a	25	c	b	a
8	a	c	b	17	a	c	b				
9	b	c	a	18	b	a	c				

70–75

You have no problem with deferred gratification, you could win prizes at it. You can wait forever for anything that you really want and nothing will put you off.

60–69

You don't have much of a problem with waiting but there are some limits to your patience. Still, you can hold out long enough to qualify for genius status.

40–59

You are not really exceptional in this department. In fact you have a decided tendency to impatience when a more considered attitude would be of help. Try to relax and let good things happen to you.

below 40

Don't go, you haven't even got your result yet!

Are you determined?

Some things in life require considerable determination. You may encounter difficulties on any path and have to overcome them. Try this test to see how you fare.

score

Do you take 'no' for an answer?

a) Not if I can help it.

b) Yes, often you have no choice but to admit defeat.

c) I try not to, but sometimes it is inevitable.

Do you have a clear idea of where you are going in life?

a) Of course, I think about it all the time.

b) No, I don't give it much consideration.

c) Yes, I think I do.

Do you always achieve your ambitions?

a) Only sometimes.

b) Yes, I never fail.

c) No, usually I mess up.

Do feel that your problems are usually solvable?

a) Yes, there is always a way.

b) Usually there's a solution.

c) Some problems just cannot be solved.

Have you ever felt like giving up on life?

a) Never, it's not my style.

b) Sometimes things get just too much.

c) Yes, I feel that way most of the time.

Do you let anyone get in the way of what you want to do?

a) I suppose so, sometimes.

b) No, it would never even cross my mind.

c) Happens to me all the time.

Does criticism deter you from your chosen path?

a) Not at all.

b) Occasionally.

c) Yes, I find it puts me off quite a lot.

score

8 Are you ambitious?
a) Not at all.
b) Moderately.
c) Yes, ambition is very important to my life.

9 Do you have a clear idea of what you want to achieve?
a) No not really.
b) I've got some idea, but I keep changing my mind.
c) Yes, I'm totally focused.

10 If necessary would you take some menial job in order to finance your real plans?
a) No, I don't think I could do that.
b) Yes, of course I would.
c) I might, but I wouldn't like it much.

11 Do you suffer fools gladly?
a) Yes, I'm really very patient.
b) Sometimes, but I try not to.
c) No, I tell them where to go.

12 Do you regard your work as far more important than the problems of others?
a) No, I think that would be arrogant.
b) Yes, I do sometimes.
c) You're damn right I do.

13 Could you ever contemplate giving up your plans and doing something less demanding?
a) I suppose I might.
b) Yes, I've certainly thought about it.
c) I'd rather die.

If you were to become seriously ill, would you still struggle to complete your work?

14

a) Yes, to my last breath.

b) No, I'd rather spend time with my family.

c) I might, but it depends on other factors.

Would you let family and friends come between you and your work?

15

a) Never, in any circumstances.

b) Yes, to a certain extent.

c) Yes, I'm very family-minded.

Would you make any personal sacrifice to complete the task you have set yourself?

16

a) No, I suppose not.

b) Yes, but there must be limits.

c) I'd do anything that it takes.

Are you at all influenced by issues such as personal comfort?

17

a) No, that never enters my head.

b) Yes, I need to be comfortable to work well.

c) I need moderate comfort but I can rough it when I need to.

Would you willingly go without sleep on a regular basis to further your work?

18

a) No, I couldn't do that.

b) Yes, it would be a very small sacrifice to make.

c) I might do, for a short while.

On a scale of 1-10, how hard driving would you say you are (1 = easy going, 10 = completely remorseless)

19

a) 1 – 3.

b) 4 – 7.

c) 8 – 10.

20

Do you think others regard you as a determined person?

a) Certainly.

b) Maybe.

c) Probably not.

21

Do you make your work occupy most of your waking life?

a) Yes, I rarely think of anything else.

b) I work a lot, but not all the time.

c) No, I don't work that much really.

22

On a scale of 1-10, how important is your work to you. (1 = Not very important at all, 10 = Almost as important as breathing.)

a) 1 – 3.

b) 4 – 7.

c) 8 – 10.

23

Do you get upset by the petty frustrations of life?

a) Yes, they drive me crazy.

b) Sometimes I get quite annoyed.

c) No, they really don't worry me that much.

24

Do you expect others to make allowances for the importance of your work?

a) No, of course not.

b) Yes, I most certainly do.

c) Sometimes it's necessary.

25

Do you feel that other people's problems take up your valuable time?

a) Yes, and it infuriates me.

b) No, I never mind.

c) It can be a pest if I'm busy.

Scoring

The maximum score is 75.

	1	2	3		1	2	3		1	2	3
1	b	c	a	10	a	c	b	19	a	b	c
2	b	c	a	11	a	b	c	20	c	b	a
3	c	a	b	12	a	b	c	21	c	b	a
4	c	b	a	13	b	a	c	22	a	b	c
5	c	b	a	14	b	c	a	23	c	b	a
6	c	a	b	15	c	b	a	24	a	c	b
7	c	b	a	16	a	b	c	25	b	c	a
8	a	b	c	17	b	c	a				
9	a	b	c	18	a	c	b				

70–75

You're so determined it's frightening. You show a ruthlessness that may well help you to succeed but will leave you with few friends. Then again, when has a genius needed friends? To you your work is everything.

60–69

You are determined and push yourself hard. You are not quite blind to things outside of work but find it hard to make time for them.

40–59

You are quite hard-driving but also appreciate the necessity of making room for others in your life. There is a softer side to your nature which people will find attractive. However, you may not have the push needed to scale the heights of genius.

below 40

You aren't taking this seriously, are you? Put your feet up! Have a good time! A genius you're not.

Are you an individualist?

People at the top tend to be rugged individualists. They often have to be because, by definition, they see things and understand things denied to the rest of us. So this test is designed to see how you shape up. Are you the sort of person who can go it alone, or do you prefer the support of friends, family and colleagues? Let's find out.

Do you like to party?
a)   No, I'd rather read a book.
b)   Try to stop me!
c)   Yes, but not too often.

1

Would you ever consider a trip to the wilderness alone?
a)   No, I'd hate the idea.
b)   I might, but I'd be worried.
c)   Yes, I'd do that and enjoy it.

2

Do you need the support of your family to bolster your confidence?
a)   Doesn't everyone?
b)   No, I love my family but my confidence is my own.
c)   To some extent but I can manage on my own when I have to.

3

Do you worry about what others think of you?
a)   Yes, of course.
b)   Well, everyone does to some extent.
c)   Never give it a thought.

4

Do you go to work partly for the company of others?
a)   Yes, I enjoy the social aspects of work.
b)   I like the occasional office party.
c)   I tend to avoid all that kind of thing.

5

Would you work alone at home?
a)   Yes, I'd love to!
b)   I might if I had to.
c)   No, it would drive me crazy.

6

Do you enjoy your own company?
a)   Yes, in fact I prefer it.
b)   I don't mind being alone.
c)   I get bored on my own.

7

score

Do you enjoy large public gatherings?

8
a) I struggle to avoid them.
b) I don't mind them in moderation.
c) I love them.

Do you enjoy playing team games?

9
a) They're my favourite.
b) I don't mind.
c) I'd rather have a tooth pulled!

Could you have swapped places with Robinson Crusoe?

10
a) Yes, that would suit me fine.
b) I'd go crazy.
c) It would be all right for a week or two.

If you could choose, which of these would you do:

11
a) Go out to a big party.
b) Have a really nice evening at home.
c) Have a few friends round for dinner.

Do you feel threatened by the presence of other people?

12
a) No, I love the company.
b) Not really, but I like my privacy as well.
c) Yes, I hate being with people more than I have to.

Would people describe you as a loner?

13
a) Who me? That's a laugh!
b) No, not really.
c) I suppose they would. What's wrong with that?

When you make a decision would you feel the need to check it with your colleagues?

14
a) What for? It's *my* decision.
b) I would always value help from colleagues.
c) I might ask if I thought it necessary.

Do you like shopping?

a) Love it! Retail therapy!

b) I'm quite keen as long as it's not too busy.

c) I have to be dragged kicking and screaming.

Would you like to live in a city or a small village?

a) I enjoy the peace of village life.

b) I wouldn't mind either. It would depend on the house.

c) I couldn't live in the country. City life is definitely my thing.

Do you take notice of opinion polls?

a) Only so that I can ignore them!

b) Yes, I often take them into account.

c) I do sometimes but I'm quite capable of making up my own mind.

Do you ever get lonely?

a) No, I like my own company.

b) Yes, quite often.

c) No, I'm never alone long enough.

In terms of contact with people, which of these jobs would suit you best:

a) Stand-up comedian.

b) Office worker.

c) Computer programmer.

How often do you go out socializing?

a) Several times a week.

b) Several times a month.

c) Seldom.

How often do you invite friends round?

a) Several times a month.

b) All the time.

c) What friends?

score

15

16

17

18

19

20

21

Do you feel threatened or nervous when you are alone?

22
a) Yes, it makes me feel very edgy.
b) Not at all.
c) A bit.

Would you take a job on a space station for a year with only two other astronauts for company?

23
a) That would be fascinating.
b) No, I couldn't cope with the isolation.
c) I'd consider it but probably would end up not going.

A wonderful house is for sale at a bargain price. The catch? It's miles from anywhere. Would you take it?

24
a) I don't care about the price, I'm not living out in the wilds.
b) I don't care about the price, I'd want to live there anyway.
c) I'd think about it.

What is the longest you have been without speaking to another person?

25
a) Days. Weeks. I really don't remember.
b) A few hours. I still remember how much I hated it.
c) A couple of days. I was glad to find company again.

Scoring

The maximum score is 75.

	1	2	3		1	2	3		1	2	3
1	b	c	a	10	b	c	a	19	a	b	c
2	a	b	c	11	a	c	b	20	a	b	c
3	a	c	b	12	a	b	c	21	b	a	c
4	a	b	c	13	a	b	c	22	a	c	b
5	a	b	c	14	b	c	a	23	b	c	a
6	c	b	a	15	a	b	c	24	a	c	b
7	c	b	a	16	c	b	a	25	b	c	a
8	c	b	a	17	b	c	a				
9	a	b	c	18	b	a	c				

70–75

You just don't need other people or value their company and opinions. You may not be popular but why should you care, you don't even know what it means. You have the self-centred approach that genius requires. No one will ever get to disrupt your work unless they come armed.

60–69

You are quite happy alone and don't really need other people much. But you're no hermit and you are not totally indifferent to others. You will find it easy to shut others out when you have to but also know how to relate to people when it suits you.

40–59

You're quite people-dependent. You don't really enjoy your own company that much and you need the love and support of friends, colleagues and relatives. You don't really have the self-sufficiency to be a genius.

below 40

You did this test with six other people at a party.

Are you inspired?

Inspiration lies at the heart of creative, problem-solving thought.
All those bright ideas are going to have to come from somewhere.
But where? Are you the sort of person who finds inspiration easily,
or do you have to cudgel your brain before it will produce each new
notion? This is a test to see just how inspired you are.

1 Do you feel that your work is inspired from 'above' (by God or by your muse, for example)?
a) Yes, of course.
b) No, not at all.
c) Maybe. I haven't given it much thought.

2 Do you get new ideas when you dream?
a) Never.
b) Occasionally.
c) Very often.

3 Do you find that valuable notions just pop into your mind at odd times of the day or night?
a) Very often.
b) It happens from time to time.
c) No, that's not how it works for me.

4 If you listen to a moving piece of music, do you find that it sparks off ideas of your own?
a) Not really.
b) Yes, music is a great source of inspiration.
c) It might do.

5 Do you find that the work of past geniuses has an inspirational effect on you?
a) Yes, of course.
b) That has happened to me.
c) No, I don't find that works for me.

6 Do you have to work hard for your ideas?
a) Yes, it's the only way.
b) No, they come easily.
c) Sometimes I'm lucky but more often it takes hard work.

score

7 Do you look at a blank sheet of paper (or empty computer screen) for hours with nothing happening?
a) No, fortunately not.
b) Like most people I get stuck sometimes.
c) It happens all the time.

8 Are there certain rituals you go through to get yourself into 'thinking mode'?
a) Yes, that helps.
b) Nothing helps me, I just have to plug away until an idea presents itself.
c) I don't need rituals, the ideas just come of their own accord.

9 Do you have to be in the right mood to get a new idea?
a) No, I don't have to be in any special mood.
b) Yes, it helps to be in the right mood.
c) There is no 'right' mood for me. It's just a hard slog.

10 Do you have the equivalent of 'writer's block' when you can't get any ideas at all?
a) Often.
b) Sometimes.
c) Never.

11 Do you have periods when the ideas come so fast that you have to work through the night to keep up with the creative flow?
a) No, unfortunately not.
b) Only very occasionally.
c) Yes, it happens quite frequently.

12 Do you use any technique, eg. meditation or yoga, to keep your creative juices flowing?
a) They don't flow, they ooze. Slowly! Techniques don't help.
b) My juices flow just fine without extra help.
c) Yes, I find some techniques do help.

13 **Are you afraid that one day the creative flow will dry up completely?**

a) Yes, it could happen.

b) I can't imagine such a thing.

c) It may have happened already.

14 **Do you find that sometimes you have to look to other people to provide your inspiration?**

a) Sometimes others can help.

b) I never need anyone else's help.

c) To be honest there is not much anyone can do to help.

15 **Is there one person, maybe your partner, who inspires you?**

a) Yes, that's true.

b) I keep telling you, I don't need help. Read my lips.

c) It's still a struggle.

16 **If you were held in solitary confinement, would your inspiration stop?**

a) Nothing but nothing stops my inspiration.

b) Yes, of course it would.

c) Who needs solitary confinement? Mine stops just fine by itself.

17 **Is your health linked to the amount of inspiration you receive?**

a) Yes, though in my case it's lack of inspiration.

b) Yes, I feel that inspiration keeps me going.

c) I'm constantly inspired and feel fantastic!

18 **A great sculptor said that his statues already existed and all he did was chip away the excess stone. Do you ever feel similarly about your work?**

a) All the time.

b) I keep chipping away and get nowhere.

c) I know what he means, but it doesn't come that easily to me.

Could you continue to live if your inspiration dried up?

19

a) No, that would be the end for me.

b) I'd struggle on somehow.

c) What do you mean 'if'?

Is there one moment in your life so far when you felt you'd had a mental breakthrough?

20

a) Yes.

b) Definitely not.

c) There have been numerous small victories.

Do other people look to you for inspiration?

21

a) They'd look in vain.

b) Yes, I'm quite flattered that sometimes they do.

c) Of course, all the time.

Edison said, 'Genius is 1% inspiration and 99% perspiration.' What do you think?

22

a) Oh yes, that's me.

b) No, Edison was a talentless slogger.

c) I suppose there's some truth in that.

Is inspiration central to your life?

23

a) Unfortunately not.

b) I'd like to think so.

c) Absolutely.

Do you find great art or great science inspiring?

24

a) Yes, though I don't *need* outside help.

b) Yes, definitely.

c) No. I find them interesting but I still have to work hard for my own ideas.

Do you seek constantly for one really huge idea?

25

a) Yes. In vain.

b) Yes, and I'm hopeful of finding it.

c) No. I've already got it.

Scoring

The maximum score is 75.

	1	2	3		1	2	3		1	2	3
1	b	c	a	10	a	b	c	19	c	b	a
2	a	b	c	11	a	b	c	20	b	c	a
3	c	b	a	12	a	c	b	21	a	b	c
4	a	c	b	13	c	a	b	22	a	c	b
5	c	b	a	14	c	a	b	23	a	b	c
6	a	c	b	15	c	a	b	24	c	b	a
7	c	b	a	16	c	b	a	25	a	b	c
8	b	a	c	17	a	b	c				
9	c	b	a	18	b	c	a				

70–75

Your inspiration is very strong. You never lack ideas, just the time to get to grips with them all.

60–69

You have a steady flow of inspiration. You realize that the flow is not unlimited but, in the end, you'll always be OK.

40–59

You have to work for your ideas. Nothing comes easily and you are often afraid that inspiration will dry up completely.

below 40

Ideas do not come to you easily, if at all.

Are you obsessive?

For most people, being obsessive is not regarded as a very attractive characteristic. It smacks a little of mental problems. People who are obsessive lack a sense of proportion and get carried away by notions that may not do them any good. However, many brilliant people ARE obsessive. They have to be or they will never achieve the level of attainment they require. Have a go at this test to see just how obsessive you really are.

1

Do you check repeatedly to see whether you locked the car?

a) Yes, always.

b) Sometimes.

c) No, I'm always sure I locked it.

2

Do you go over your work ceaselessly to try to find mistakes?

a) No, I do a quick check then let it go.

b) Yes, that's me, I can never check enough.

c) I check things over a few times but eventually you have to let it go.

3

Would you hesitate forever before letting someone else examine your work?

a) No, it's not a problem for me.

b) Yes, I hate that point where you have to let someone else look at your work.

c) I know what you mean, but it's not a major problem.

4

Do you sometimes have notions that you just cannot let go of?

a) No, that doesn't happen to me.

b) It has happened but not a lot.

c) Yes, I feel like that a lot.

5

Do you have ideas that seem more important to you than anything else?

a) Of course, doesn't everyone?

b) No, that's not a problem I have.

c) Some of my ideas seem pretty important but I may be wrong.

6

Do you sometimes get so involved in what you're doing that you forget to eat?

a) No, that's never happened.

b) Very occasionally.

c) I miss meals all the time like that.

7 Have you ever worked so hard on something that you discover you stayed up all night without meaning to?

a) Yes, I frequently forget to go to bed.

b) No, I'm always ready for bed at the same time.

c) It has happened from time to time.

8 Are there certain things which you just have to do, although there is no logical reason for your actions?

a) Yes, it can be embarrassing but I can't stop it.

b) No, I don't do that.

c) I have had that experience but not often.

9 Do you get stuck with one thought to the exclusion of all else?

a) Not really.

b) From time to time.

c) Yes, that's just the way I am.

10 Are you sometimes unaware of what goes on around you because you are so involved in what you are doing?

a) Yes, that's me all over.

b) No, that's not the way I am.

c) It happens occasionally.

11 Will you follow a train of thought even though others try to convince you it is misguided?

a) Yes, once I start nothing's going to stop me.

b) I'm like that sometimes.

c) No, that really isn't me.

12 Have people told you that you tend to become obsessive about things?

a) No, I don't get told that.

b) It has been mentioned.

c) Yes, that's said about me all the time.

13. Are there issues that you just cannot leave alone even though pursuing them is of no obvious benefit to you?

a) No, I would know when to stop.

b) I recognize that situation.

c) That's me all the time.

14. Does one issue dominate your whole life?

a) Of course.

b) Not at all.

c) Yes, though I can switch off when I need to.

15. Do you find it hard to switch off from things you think are important?

a) Yes, switching off isn't in my nature.

b) It's usually possible for me to switch off.

c) No, I that isn't a problem.

16. Do you find yourself checking and re-checking the details of what you have done?

a) I do that compulsively.

b) I sometimes do it but can usually stop myself.

c) No I'm never tempted to do that.

17. On a scale of 1 – 10, how obsessive do you think you are? (1 = really laid back, 10 = totally obsessive)

a) 1 – 3.

b) 4 – 7.

c) 8 – 10.

18. Does your tendency to get stuck with one thought irritate people?

a) Yes, hugely.

b) No, I don't think so.

c) Sometimes.

19 Have you ever had medical treatment for obsessive/
compulsive disorders?

score

a) Yes.
b) No.
c) It was a long time ago.

20 Have your obsessions ever had a detrimental effect on
your life?

a) No, certainly not.
b) Yes, unfortunately.
c) Once or twice.

21 Have you ever wished that you could be less caught up
in the issues which concern you?

a) Yes, often.
b) No, never.
c) Sometimes.

22 Do you ever feel satisfied that you have done enough work
on a project?

a) No, not at all.
b) Yes, eventually.
c) Of course.

23 Do you find it quite impossible just to let go?

a) Yes.
b) No.
c) Sometimes.

24 Have people broken off relationships with you because of
your obsessive behaviour?

a) Yes, I'm afraid that has happened to me repeatedly.
b) No, I've never had that misfortune.
c) Yes, it has happened, but not often.

25

Do you regard your single-mindedness as a great asset?

a) Yes, I find it invaluable.

b) No, that isn't one of my virtues.

c) It's quite useful, but I'm not that single-minded.

Scoring

The maximum score is 75.

	1	2	3		1	2	3		1	2	3
1	c	b	a	10	b	c	a	19	b	c	a
2	a	c	b	11	c	b	a	20	a	c	b
3	a	c	b	12	a	b	c	21	b	c	a
4	a	b	c	13	a	b	c	22	c	b	a
5	b	c	a	14	b	c	a	23	b	c	a
6	a	b	c	15	c	b	a	24	b	c	a
7	b	c	a	16	c	b	a	25	b	c	a
8	b	c	a	17	a	b	c				
9	a	b	c	18	b	c	a				

70–75

You have the obsessive quality needed to become a genius, but beware of sliding into mental illness because of your obsessions.

60–69

You're very obsessive but not entirely blind to other issues. You are aware that there may be dangers in being so single-minded.

40–59

You are quite obsessive on certain subjects but are well aware that there are many other things that should occupy your mind.

below 40

Forget it! You have the mental tension of a shrimping net.

Literary quiz

A knowldege of literature may not be proof of ability but, on the other hand, you would expect a would-be literary genius to have a pretty good knowledge of his or her competitors. This test is tough but, if you have pretensions to literary greatness, you'll need to do well in it. If you're the scientific type we'll let you off. For now.

1. Which poet, known as the Golden Boy, killed himself and, in doing so, gave rise to a famous painting?

2. Who wrote of, "Merely innocent flirtation, not quite adultery but adulteration"?

3. Who wrote, "Mordre wol out; that se we day by day"?

4. Which Shakespeare king said, "I wasted time and now doth time waste me."?

5. Who wrote a huge work in several parts entitled, *In Search of Lost Time*?

6. Which imaginary castle was created by Mervyn Peake?

7. Which book features a desert island, some lost choir boys, and a pig's head on a stake?

8. Which English novel of the Revolution takes place in Paris and London?

9. Who wrote of a slough called Despond?

10. Which brothers were immortalized in a novel by Dostoevsky?

11. Which English novelist wrote: "England's not a bad country... It's just a mean, cold, ugly, divided, tired, clapped-out, post-imperial, post-industrial, slag-heap covered in polystyrene hamburger cartons."?

12. Who compiled the first English dictionary?

13. Which author was primarily responsible for popularizing the legend of King Arthur?

14. Who wrote *The Magic Mountain*?

15. In which book did Maugham write, "People ask you for criticism, but they only want praise."?

16. From which epic poem (and by whom) do these lines come: "The infernal serpent; he it was, whose guile stirred up with envy and revenge, deceived the mother of mankind."

17. Who wrote *The Dunciad*?

18. Tennyson wrote a poem named after a royal personage. Who was it?

19. Who wrote,"Rose is a rose is a rose is a rose, is a rose."?

20. Who says in which play by which author, "To lose one parent, Mr Worthing, may be regarded as a misfortune, to lose both looks like carelessness."

21. Who wrote an ode entitled *Intimations of Mortality*?

22. By what name did Samuel Langhorne Clemens find literary fame?

23. Which Philip Roth novel featured a notorious piece of liver?

24. According to Mark Twain familiarity breeds contempt – and what else?

25. In which book is it said, "All animals are equal but some animals are more equal than others."?

26. In which novel of the future would you find Bernard Marx and a Native American ?

27. Who wrote *Prometheus Unbound*?

28. Who wrote,"There is no greater pain than to remember a happy time when one is in misery."?

29. Which novel begins, "Last night I dreamt I went to Manderley again."

30. Which woman author wrote a series of novels about Ancient Greece?

Scoring

25–30

Excellent. You can at least sound like a genius!

20–24

You have a wide knowledge of literature.

15–19

Not bad, but not great.

10–14

Average.

Below 10

You're not a literary culture-vulture.

1. Chatterton. 2. Byron (in Don Juan). 3. Chaucer. 4. Richard II. 5. Proust. 6. Gormenghast. 7. Lord of the Flies. 8. Dickens' 'A Tale of Two Cities'. 9. John Bunyan in 'The Pilgrim's Progress' 10. The Brothers Karamazov. 11. Margaret Drabble. 12. Dr Samuel Johnson. 13. Sir Thomas Malory. 14. Thomas Mann. 15. 'Of Human Bondage.' 16. John Milton, 'Paradise Lost'. 17. Alexander Pope. 18. 'The Princess.' 19. Gertrude Stein (in 'Sacred Emily'). 20. Lady Brackhell in Oscar Wilde's The Importance of Being Earnest'. 21. Wordsworth. 22. Mark Twain. 23. 'Portnoy's Complaint'. 24. Children. 25. 'Animal Farm' by George Orwell. 26. 'Brave New World'. 27. P.B. Shelley. 28. Dante. 29. 'Rebecca' by Daphne Du Maurier. 30. Mary Renault.

Music quiz

You may not know much about music but, in the search to be a well-rounded individual, you should have at least a passing knowledge of some of the greatest works ever produced by the human mind. Try this quiz to see how you shape up.

1. Who wrote the opera The Rape of Lucretia?

2. Under which name is Bruckner's Fourth Symphony known?

3. Which of Bach's compositions is an exploration of counterpoint?

4. Which of Franck's symphonic poems is about a count eternally chased by demon because of going hunting on the Sabbath?

5. Who wrote the *Glagolitic Mass*?

6. In which film did the Adagietto from Mahler's Fifth Symphony feature?

7. From which Puccini opera does the tune *Nessun Dorma* originate?

8. What is Tchaikovsky's Seventh Symphony known as?

9. What male character sings a bird-like part in *The Magic Flute*?

10. Which of Haydn's symphonies is known as the *Farewell Symphony*?

11. Who wrote *Fantasia para un gentilhombre*?

12. In which Verdi opera does the character Manrico appear?

13. Who wrote the libretto to Don Giovanni?

14. What is the name of the heroine in Tchaikovsky's *Eugene Onegin*?

15. What is unusual about Beehoven's Eighth's Symphony?

16. Under which name is Mozart's Symphony K.385 known?

17. How many symphonies did Sibelius write?

18. Which part of Smetana's *Ma Vlast* desribes the river flowing through Prague?

19. Who wrote the opera *Ariadne auf Naxos*?

20. Which of Verdi's operas focused on an Ethiopian slave girl?

21. What is the name of the prison governor in Beethoven's *Fidelio*?

22. What is the name of Stravinsky's ballet that started his neo-classical period?

23. Under which name is Schuman's First Symphony known?

24. Who wrote the song cycle *Die Schone Mallerin*?

25. Which Wagner opera contains the character Hans Sachs?

26. Which orchestral suite contains *Anitra's Dance*?

27. Who wrote the symphonic poem *The Noonday Witch*?

28. Which composer produced the most successful orchestration of Mussorgsky's *Pictures at an Exhibition*?

29. From which opera does the *Dance of the Polovtsian Maidens* originate?

30. What is the final part in Wagner's *Der Ring des Nibelungen*?

Scoring

The maximum score is 30.

25–30

Excellent. You have a good knowledge of the works of genius.

20–24

Still very good. The quiz isn't easy and you have acquitted yourself with honour.

15–19

Music is not your preferred area but, even so, your general knowledge is quite reasonable.

10–14

A bit of study might help here. Your knowledge is really quite sketchy and could do with improvement.

Below 10

Classical music is not for you. Try something else.

1. Benjamin Britten. 2. The Romantic. 3. The Art of Fugue. 4. Le Chasseur Maudit. 5. Leos Janacek. 6. Death in Venice. 7. Turandot. 8. Manfred. 9. Papageno. 10. No. 45. 11. Joaquin Rodrigo. 12. Il Trovatore. 13. Lorenzo da Ponte. 14. Tatyana. 15. It contains no slow movements. 16. Haffner. 17. Seven. 18. Vltava. 19. Richard Strauss. 20. Aida. 21. Pizarro. 22. Pulcinella. 23. Spring. 24. Franz Schubert. 25. The Meistersinger von Nurnberg. 26. Grieg's Peer Gynt Suite No.1. 27. Antonin Dvorak. 28. Maurice Ravel. 29. 'Prince Igor' by Alexander Borodin. 30. Gotterdammerung.

Philosophy quiz

Philosophy deals with the secrets of existence, the why of life.
Plenty of people are happy to leave such questions to the great
philosophers. To have a real understanding of your own existence
however, you need to think about it a bit. Here is your chance to
evaluate your philosophical understanding.

1. Which Greek philosopher supervised the education of the young Alexander of Macedon (later to be Alexander the Great)?

2. Which Breton philosopher, author of *Know Thyself*, is mainly remembered for his tragic love affair and subsequent castration?

3. What name is given to the Theory of Knowledge?

4. What name is given to the study of the nature of being?

5. Who stated, "Cogito, ergo sum"?

6. Which branch of philosophy deals with the nature of morality?

7. Who wrote *The Critique of Pure Reason*?

8. Which pupil of Socrates wrote *The Republic*?

9. What name is given to the moral view that the only thing that is good is pleasure?

10. With which philosophy would you associate Kierkegaard, Sartre, and Heidegger?

11. Which philosophical term originally meant 'the art of conversation, discussion or debate'?

12. Which American linguist wrote Language and Mind in 1968?

13. With which philosophy do we associate Diogenes?

14. What name is often given to the employment of methods based on practical experience rather than on an accepted body of theory?

15. Which Scot wrote *A Treatise of Human Nature* in 1737?

16. Who is regarded as the foremost philosophical and religious figure of Ancient China?

17. Which German philosopher lived in the late 17th and early 18th centuries, invented a calculating machine which won him membership of the Royal Society in Britain?

18. Which Somerset-born philosopher wrote an *Essay Concerning Human Understanding*?

19. Which philosopher was born in Amsterdam of Jewish parents and was brought up to speak Spanish, Portuguese and Hebrew but was never very good at speaking Dutch?

20. Which philosophy was founded by Zeno of Citium?

21. Which philosophical movement did Husserl found?

22. What common name is given to 'the theory of the conditions of valid inference'?

23. Which British philosopher, the godson of John Stuart Mill, was closely involved with the Campaign for Nuclear Disarmament?

24. Which movement emanated from the Vienna Circle?

25. Which philosophy takes the view that "man is the measure of all things"?

26. Which Spanish Jewish philosopher wrote *The Guide of the Perplexed*?

27. Which English mathematician gave his name to a recognized branch of algebra?

28. Who wrote the *Communist Manifesto*?

29. Which Frenchman is most frequently associated with 'deconstruction'?

30. Which philosophy holds that physical objects can have no existence apart from a mind that which is conscious of them?

Scoring

The maximum score is 30.

25–30
Brilliant! Your knowledge of the subject is first rate.

20–24
Very good. You have a superior knowledge of the subject and are at home with most of the important philosophical concepts.

15–19
Not bad, but you need to study more.

10–14
You are really not up to standard on this one. Try taking evening classes.

Below 10
You think Ethics is a place near London.

1. Aristotle. 2. Peter Abelard. 3. Epistemology 4. Ontology 5. Descartes. 6. Ethics. 7. Kant. 8. Plato. 9. Hedonism. 10. Existentialism. 11. Dialectic. 12. Chomsky. 13. Cynicism 14. Empiricism. 15. Hume. 16. Confucius. 17. Leibniz. 18. Locke. 19. Spinoza. 20. Stoicism. 21. Phenomenology 22. Logic. 23. Russell. 24. Logical Positivism 25. Relativism. 26. Maimonides. 27. Boole. 28. Marx. 29. Derrida. 30. Idealism.

Test Forty

Science

In the modern world, our lives and realities are increasingly dominated by science. You just can't safely decide "I'm an artist and don't know about that sort of thing" any more. Try your scientific knowledge with this test.

1. What does DNA stand for?

2. Which are the only cells of the human body that have no nucleus?

3. What does LASER stand for?

4. What is fission?

5. According to relativity, what happens to moving clocks?

6. What is a chaotic system?

7. What are the Four Forces in order of strength?

8. What do GUT and TOE stand for?

9. What substance causes the soreness in muscles used for heavy exercise?

10. Photosynthesis is the inverse of ———.

11. If you live in the US, how fast do the generators at your local power station turn?

12. What is another name for natural magnets, of the type made of iron?

13. What, according to relativity, happens to light passing near the sun?

14. Most of the mass of an atom, but almost none of its volume, lies in its ———.

15. Name the 'Oldest Human Ancestor', an australopithecine.

16. Name the Polish woman who was one of the founders of nuclear science.

17. What are the basic building blocks of carbohydrates?

18. The word 'cell' was first used in a biological sense by which English physicist?

19. How much of their DNA do humans share with other individuals?

20. What biological material was first analyzed by Antoine van Leeuwenhoek?

21. What temperature is normally considered to be absolute zero?

22. How close has anyone ever got to absolute zero in a laboratory?

23. How long ago did dinosaurs become extinct?

24. The gene for six fingers is dominant over the gene for five fingers. True or false?

25. The gene is the basic unit of what?

26. What is special about the bacteria known as Chlamydia and Rickettsia?

27. If someone dies after a fight or after being severely frightened, rigor mortis sets in more quickly. True or false?

28. Does helium come from the Earth's atmosphere?

29. What happens when electrical charges accelerate?

30. What can the human body detect that the human eye cannot?

Scoring

The maximum score is 30.

25–30
You have a very profound knowledge of modern scientific thinking. This is clearly a field in which you feel quite at home and where you can exercise your abilities to the full.

20–24
You are well versed in much of modern science but still have much more to learn. This is clearly an area which you find fascinating and where you can make the most of your talent.

15–19
You have moderate scientific knowledge. As a background to some other field of activity this would be useful, but you are not equipped to make science your main occupation.

10–14
Science is not really for you. Try the other tests, there must be areas you find far more congenial.

Below 10
Your scientific knowledge could only be found with the aid of a rather powerful microscope.

---

1. Deoxyribonucleic acid. 2. Red blood cells. 3. Light Amplification by Stimulated Emission of Radiation. 4. A process that splits a large nucleus into two or more smaller daughter nuclei. 5. They slow down. 6. One in which the final outcome depends very sensitively on the initial conditions. 7. Strong, Electromagnetic, Weak, Gravity. 8. The Grand Unified Theory, and the Theory of Everything. 9. Lactic acid. 10. Respiration. 11. 60 times per second (electrical current in the USA is rated at 60 Hertz). 12. Ferromagnets. 13. It gets bent. 14. Nucleus. 15. Lucy. 16. Marie Curie. 17. Sugars. 18. Robert Hooke. 19. 99.8% of a degree. 23. 65 million years. 24. True. 25. Heredity. 26. They are 20. Human sperm. 21. -273.17 degrees Celsius. 22. Within one billionth the smallest living things. 28. No, it is found trapped with oil and natural gas. 29. Electromagnetic waves are produced. 30. Infrared radiation.

Assess your vocabulary

A large vocabulary has always been regarded as a sign not only of high intelligence but also of the ability to channel your brain power in useful ways. If you can juggle with verbal concepts, you are likely to be able to handle ideas effectively and communicate them to others with ease. This test is designed to test your word power to the limit. The words are all quite difficult but are all in regular use. We have avoided words that are archaic or only used in dialect. See how many you get right. In each case you must look at the first word in each group and find another word similar in meaning to it.

		A	B	C	D
1.	PRAGMATIC	Political	Accurate	Practical	Civil
2.	EPICURE	Philosopher	Author	Fraudster	Gourmet
3.	GRADATION	Degree	Height	Veracity	Dexterity
4.	HETERODOX	Rigid	Varied	Unfair	Unconventional
5.	SABBATIZE	Ritualize	Confirm	Bless	Organize
6.	ENDEMIC	Popular	Native	Thoughtful	Final
7.	ENDOGAMOUS	Friendly	Matrimonial	Free	Grateful
8.	HASLET	Jerkin	Relation	Entrails	Armor
9.	GALACTIC	Milky	Astronomical	Stellar	Huge
10.	LASSITUDE	Heat	Overeating	Faintness	Verbiage
11.	LEPID	Cool	Weak	Unkind	Pleasant
12.	DARIOLE	Mold	Forge	Decoration	Dagger
13.	FALCATE	Tremble	Crossed	Sickly	Sickle-like
14.	GEMINATE	Doubled	Bejewelled	Flourishing	Growing
15.	MORPHEW	Leaf	Vein	Sacrifice	Skin eruption
16.	PROTOPLASM	Living matter	Organism	Cell wall	Erudition
17.	PROPRIETY	Decency	Rulership	Efficiency	Courage
18.	SESSILE	Fragile	Sedentary	Straight	Pleated
19.	PROSAIC	Thoughtful	Dull	Hopeful	Varied
20.	MONOLITH	Pillar	Arch	Building	Construction
21.	PELTA	Roof	Shield	Sword	Verse
22.	JUGATE	Unusual	Decent	Paired	Forgotten
23.	CRAPULENCE	Dishonesty	Boasting	Sickness	Violence
24.	EXTIRPATE	Destroy	Forget	Flee	Forgive
25.	GESTALT	Recognition	Pattern	Shadow	Area

26. INCRESCENT	Large	Slow	Bright	Waxing
27. MORDACIOUS	Biting	Wicked	Extreme	Gleeful
28. ONUS	Honor	Burden	Rebate	Penalty
29. COAPT	Dense	Slow	Join	Formal
30. ESTOP	Cork	Preclude	Terminus	Here
31. FROTTAGE	Rubbing	Embroidery	Parsimony	Rejoicing
32. KITH	Relatives	Friends	Knowledge	Peel
33. GABELLE	Ornament	Jewel	Tax	Toy
34. DURUM	Wheat	Plenty	Pleasure	Soil
35. LIMPID	Cold	Poor	Depraved	Clear
36. MORIBUND	Dying	Poorly	Sash	Belt
37. PENCHANT	Hanging	Bias	Mirror	Overhang
38. PUTATIVE	Unconfirmed	Untried	Powerless	Reputed
39. MEPHITIS	Inflammation	Growth	Stink	Infection
40. INCHOATE	Angry	Worried	Incomplete	Sideways
41. GENITIVE	Possessive	Giving birth	Delayed	Productive
42. JEJUNE	Yellowed	Valuable	Doubtful	Spiritless
43. FETTLE	Order	Chain	Control	Mend
44. MORSURE	Bite	Lace	Cinch	Corruption
45. INVEIGLE	Contradict	Invent	Entice	Dispute
46. INVEIGH	Humiliate	Forbid	Destroy	Attack
47. PINION	Wing	Stake	Breath	Consume
48. NEFANDOUS	False	Gloating	Stolen	Abominable
49. LENTIGO	Vegetable	Freckle	Mouse	Framework
50. FABIAN	Indecisive	Cowardly	Delaying	Secret

Scoring

1. C	11. D	21. B	31. A	41. A
2. D	12. A	22. C	32. B	42. D
3. A	13. D	23. C	33. C	43. A
4. D	14. A	24. A	34. A	44. A
5. A	15. D	25. B	35. D	45. C
6. B	16. A	26. D	36. A	46. D
7. B	17. A	27. A	37. B	47. A
8. C	18. B	28. B	38. D	48. D
9. D	19. B	29. C	39. C	49. B
10. C	20. A	30. B	40. C	50. C

The maximum score is 50.

Over 45

This is a tough test and if you scored over 45 your vocabulary is absolutely excellent. You probably work with words professionally and solve crossword puzzles with an ease that infuriates your friends.

35–44

If you scored between 35 and 44 your score is still very good indeed. You have a vocabulary well outside the normal range.

25–34

A score of 25-34 is extremely creditable and would indicate quite a good command of the language.

15–24

A score of 15-24 would be about average. The test did contain quite a few common words which, though you might not use them every day, would be in the vocabulary of an educated person.

Below 15

Below 15, you could do with working on your word power.

Assess your verbal reasoning

One of the key indicators of intelligence, verbal reasoning is the ability to assess and compare concepts to recognize patterns. See how you do with this test.

Flex your verbal dexterity with the test below.

1. Brick is to House as Branch is to:
a) Wood   b) Tree   c) Hut   d) Mouse   e) Flower

2. Wet is to Arid as Sick is to:
a) Healthy   b) Right   c) Malady   d) Sane   e) Dry

3. Apple is to Tomato as Turnip is to:
a) Carrot   b) Bread   c) Plum   d) Avocado   e) Bowl

4. Pestle is to Mortar as Motte is to:
a) Water   b) Building   c) Peat   d) Forest   e) Bailey

5. Vapor is to Precipitation as Cocoon is to:
a) Cold   b) Exterior   c) Pupa   d) Spray   e) Silk

6. Bambino is to Adult as Sapling is to:
a) Oak   b) Branch   c) Wood   d) Tree   e) Table

7. Culmination is to Start as Summit is to:
a) Peak   b) Base   c) Height   d) Snow   e) Mountain

8. Stale is to Originality as Compromise is to:
a) Concede   b) Lie   c) Resolute   d) Agree   e) Apologize

9. Marathon is to Stamina as Fire is to:
a) Smoke   b) Flame   c) Light   d) Fuel   e) Ash

10. Leaf is to Book as Yolk is to:
a) Bond   b) White   c) Egg   d) Hen   e) Hatch

11. Effeminate is to Man as Tomboy is to:
a) Bairn   b) Girl   c) Gentle   d) Balance   e) Straight

12. Depilate is to Hair as Mow is to:
a) Cut   b) Field   c) Soil   d) Grass   e) Trim

13. Temperature is to Degree as Distance is to:
a) Meter   b) Remote   c) Time   d) Space   e) Separate

14. Material is to Tangible as Theory is to:

a) Rule   b) Abstract   c) Argument   d) Explain   e) Idea

15. Challenge is to Stretch as Elongate is to:

a) Shrink   b) Question   c) Dismiss   d) Lengthen   e) Multiply

Are you well warmed up now? Stretch out with another word work out: spot the imposter in each of the groups below.

16. a) Conformist   b) Orthodox   c) Traditionalist
     d) Dissident   e) Acquiescent

17. a) Supercilious   b) Contemptuous   c) Denigrating
     d) Laudation   e) Depreciating

18. a) Tradition   b) Reformation   c) Revolution
     d) Innovation   e) Transposition

19. a) Incessant   b) Unremitting   c) Resistance
     d) Sustained   e) Continual

20. a) Proficient   b) Punctual   c) Competent
     d) Capable   e) Ambidextrous

21. a) Captive   b) Detainee   c) Trusty
     d) Prisoner   e) Custodian

22. a) Coerce   b) Compel   c) Coalesce
     d) Enforce   e) Bludgeon

23. a) Duce   b) Autocrat   c) Despot
     d) Tyrant   e) Riposte

24. a) Retaliate   b) Avenge   c) Enforce
     d) Requite   e) Recompense

25. a) Enumerate   b) Paginate   c) Calculate
     d) Cipher   e) Figure

26. a) Idiosyncrasy   b) Eccentricity   c) Foible
     d) Mannerism   e) Philanthropy

27. a) Classify   b) Categorize   c) Rank
    d) Compile   e) Place

28. a) Median   b) Mainstream   c) Midrib
    d) Equidistant   e) Centre

29. a) Patter   b) Lingo   c) Index
    d) Dialect   e) Idiom

30. a) Premeditated   b) Spontaneous   c) Makeshift
    d) Improvised   e) Impromptu

Scoring

1. b	2. a	3. a	4. e	5. e	6. d	7. b
8. c	9. d	10. c	11. b	12. d	13. a	14. b
15. d	16. d	17. d	18. a	19. c	20. b	21. e
22. c	23. e	24. c	25. b	26. e	27. d	28. b
29. c	30. a					

Over 25
25 or over is excellent.

Over 20
Over 20 is very creditable.

15–19
Your verbal skills are satisfactory.

Below 15
Below 15 suggests you could benefit from some attention in this area.

Do you have a creative personality?

Creativity and originality of thought are traits intrinsic to genius.
But these skills may be of little consequence in isolation. Topicality
and plausibility are both prerequisites for any blast of creativity to be
useful, along with a sheer determination to persist regardless of any
setbacks.

Creativity can be interpreted in different ways. Eminent talents have
boasted different skills: Shakespeare (literary), Einstein (scientific),
Mozart (musical). The questions below aim to gauge your creative
abilities, but you should recognize that your creativity may also be
manifested in different forms. Judge for yourself by attempting the
following tests.

These questions are intended as a quick taster - judge for yourself the creative subject matter closest to your own heart.

score

Do you find brainstorming:

1

a) tortuous – you find it difficult coming up with ideas quickly.
b) stimulating – you find your mind working quicker than your pen can.
c) useful, especially with others – you are most able to bounce ideas around when others contribute their own and help take yours forward.

During the course of daily grind, be it following a recipe or attempting a bit of DIY, does the lack of a listed material result in you:

2

a) feeling frustrated and searching for a substitute. Attempts to adapt procedures by using the substitute usually go wrong.
b) going out to buy the exact material required before continuing.
c) effortlessly adapting to either making the most of what you have or quickly reaching for a substitute. You generally reach the desired result.

You purchase something requiring simple home assembly, but later discover the instructions are in Japanese (and you're a little rusty). Are you most likely to:

3

a) lay out all the components and figure out what goes where and how. It usually works.
b) contact the retailer and demand comprehensive English written instructions. Otherwise, ask for a refund.
c) elicit some help from a willing, practically-minded friend.

Do you find works of art:

4

a) boring. You can't understand the point of them, and find it difficult to gauge their quality.
b) fascinating. You find it easy to lose yourself in the imagery of an abstract painting and able to offer various interpretations.
c) interesting but your attention span is limited. You tend to buy the guidebook to facilitate understanding of different works.

Popular belief states that everyone has a novel hiding in them somewhere. Does the prospect of writing a book leave you:

5

a) excited. You love words and enjoy expressing yourself with a colorful vocabulary. You find it easy to imagine storylines and fantasies.
b) challenged. Much as you would like your fifteen minutes of fame, you would seek much of your inspiration from past experience. Filling a whole book would take some considerable time and effort.
c) uninspired. You may enjoy reading, but would prefer to leave the effort of writing to some other more imaginative soul.

Which of the following typical types of examination question do you prefer:

a) a specific question with multiple choice answers.
b) an open-ended question open to different interpretation and answerable in an essay format.
c) questions relating to, and applying information/facts given in the question.

Which of the following activities do you find the most fulfilling:

a) watching television.
b) reading.
c) writing.

For the musicians amongst you, when playing your chosen instrument, do you prefer to:

a) read sheet music and adhere to the manuscript.
b) improvise with a group of like-minded musicians.
c) play by ear, reproducing what you've heard, embellishing wherever possible.

Struck by an idea provoking you to ask why hasn't someone thought of that before, are you most likely to:

a) action your idea with a bit of research and deeper thought, initiating some lively debate if nothing more tangible is possible.
b) shrug it off, deeming it not worthy of further thought, preferring to think about lunch instead.
c) engross yourself for a while longer in your thoughts before getting distracted – your intention to return to it is normally in vain.

Do you consider yourself:

10

a) innovative – you dislike following rules and tried and tested methods and procedures.
b) a follower – you prefer to follow the accepted method of doing something, but are willing to lend your support to others' ideas if convinced of their validity.
c) indifferent – you are a laid-back, relaxed individual who just 'goes along with whatever'.

Scoring

The higher the score, the higher the creativity

1.	a) 0	b) 2	c) 1
2.	a) 1	b) 0	c) 2
3.	a) 2	b) 0	c) 1
4.	a) 0	b) 2	c) 1
5.	a) 2	b) 1	c) 0
6.	a) 0	b) 2	c) 1
7.	a) 0	b) 1	c) 2
8.	a) 0	b) 2	c) 1
9.	a) 2	b) 0	c) 1
10.	a) 2	b) 1	c) 0

Maximum Score is 20

17-20

This would suggest that you are a highly creative person with plenty of original ideas.

13-16

This is a very good score which could be improved with practice.

9-12

This suggests that you need to work hard on improving your creativity.

Below 9

This indicates that creativity is not your strongest point.

Test Forty Four

Can you concentrate?

Find yourself a quiet corner and try and banish everyday concerns from your mind. Now get started. Consider the following situations, and select (honestly!) the response you would most likely adapt.

1 During the course of everyday conversation, how often do you find yourself asking "now, where was I?":

a) Never. b) Often. c) Occasionally.

2 You're ploughing through a challenging scientific article. Are you most likely to:

a) Drift off into a daydream early on and give up to avoid wasting more time.

b) focus wholeheartedly on the text and absorb fully most of what you've read.

c) manage a few minutes before realizing you don't know what you've just read and have to recap.

3 Imagine yourself working in a busy, open plan office. Would you find yourself:

a) able to shut out the many distractions, forcing yourself to focus entirely on the task at hand.
b) highly unproductive – your attention would wander to the noise and movement around you.
c) able to work in short bursts, with attention lapses here and there.

4 Do you work best:

a) with a steady hum of background noise.
b) in any environment – you rarely notice what is or isn't going on if you're deep in thought.
c) in total silence.

You're watching a rather dull documentary relevant to your work. How much are you most likely to absorb and remember afterwards?

5

a) little – you "switched off" early on in proceedings.
b) the majority – you would have a good overall picture with a handful of hard facts to quote.
c) a more fragmented impression – your mind has a tendency to wander.

Would you describe yourself as:

6

a) having a good attention span – if you need to focus, you will.
b) able to apply yourself and your attention to stimulating subject matter, but less so for the more mundane.
c) unable to concentrate wholeheartedly on anything for more than a few minutes at most.

After being introduced to a fellow guest at a party, are you most likely to:

7

a) find yourself surreptitiously asking for a reminder a little later as you failed to take his/her name in the first time.
b) remember the guest's name a week later without prompting.
c) get the name half right a bit later – your mind was not entirely focused on the pleasantries.

You have been commissioned to write a lengthy article on a topic close to your heart. With a week to complete the work, would you:

a) start immediately, able to maintain clarity and work efficiently to finish well before the deadline.
b) Procrastinate for a few days and then rush the article off, working through the night to meet the deadline.
c) set yourself a rigid timetable, adhered to most of the time, but sometimes you find yourself unable to focus and in need of a break.

9. Does everyday life find you most likely to be:

a) dashing constantly between jobs, leaving some unfinished as you flit from one thing to another.
b) focusing entirely on the job at hand and finishing as much as possible before embarking on something else.
c) focusing on more than one thing at a time – it may take a little longer than doing each individually but at least you don't get bored.

10. Do you find yourself daydreaming:

a) regularly – and not without some considerable embarrassment.
b) rarely – you are usually too focused on whatever you are doing at the time.
c) sometimes – but only when you find yourself doing something particularly tedious.

11 How often have you been asked a question and been compelled to ask for it to be repeated as you weren't listening?

a) a few times.   b) frequently.   c) rarely, if ever.

12 Would you find taking the minutes of an interminable meeting:

a) rather onerous, but your mind would be on the job.
b) a task requiring considerable effort to minimize the inevitable inaccuracies you make.
c) impossible – you would never be able to concentrate on everything and are much more proficient delegating the job to someone else.

13 How often do you find yourself muttering "it's no good, I just can't concentrate"?
a) regularly – regardless of the environment you are in.
b) sometimes – normally provoked by some intrusive physical disturbance.
c) rarely – you are adept at applying yourself whenever you deem it necessary.

14 You're working on a challenging and rather convoluted project in a team. Are you most likely to be the person:

a) trying in vain to focus your fellow team members on the task, loath to digress.
b) trying to "liven things up" – whether dropping in a tasty morsel of gossip or suggesting a coffee break.
c) contributing to the discussion now and again, having to refocus whenever you realize your mind has wandered.

15 How often do you find yourself slamming on the brakes of your car or stopping yourself in your tracks when you realize your concentration has lapsed and someone is in your way?

score

a) all the time.   b) now and again.   c) hardly ever.

16 You receive some surprising (but not troublesome) news of a personal nature. Next day at work are you:

a) able to carry on as normal, blocking out the revelations until your working day is over.
b) of little use – your mind is buzzing with the news and attempts to concentrate on work are futile.
c) slightly less productive than normal – attention may wander, but once you realize this, you revert your focus to work.

17 Do you find deadlines:

a) the cause of much anguish – despite attempting to focus on the task, you find yourself distracted by continually determining how much time you have left.
b) of little consequence – depending on your level of interest, you generally find it easy to settle down and work until a task is completed.
c) a helpful motivator – the nearer the deadline, the better you can concentrate as you realize the work has to get done.

You find yourself embroiled in a verbal conflict: your partner swears s/he told you something of which you have no recollection and claim s/he didn't. Is it most likely that:

18
a) you were told but you weren't paying attention at the time.
b) your partner is confused and actually told someone else – you always listen attentively.
c) you were told but immediately deemed it of no consequence and have since forgotten.

You are undertaking an arduous calculation with the help of your calculator where you must sum a long string of numbers. Is this:

19
a) slightly frustrating – you find yourself having to do it again as you forgot where you were.
b) a nightmare – you find yourself unsure as to whether you have entered certain numbers and end up doing it six times before getting two totals which tally.
c) unproblematic – you ensure you are uninterrupted and feel confident with your first result.

You spend a relaxing evening watching a gripping thriller with a web of sub-plots running through. Are you likely to:

20
a) have a decent overall idea of the storyline, but remain a bit unsure of the complete picture.
b) be bombarded with questions demanding to know what's going on as you're the one most likely to know.
c) be the one doing most of the bombarding.

Scoring

The maximum score is 40.

	a	b	c		a	b	c		a	b	c
1.	2	0	1	8.	2	0	1	15.	0	1	2
2.	0	2	1	9.	0	2	1	16.	2	0	1
3.	2	0	1	10.	0	2	1	17.	0	2	1
4.	1	2	0	11.	1	0	2	18.	0	2	1
5.	0	2	1	12.	2	1	0	19.	1	0	2
6.	2	1	0	13.	0	1	2	20.	1	2	0
7.	0	2	1	14.	2	0	1				

35–40

You obviously have excellent concentration and are able to bring your full mental faculties to bear on any task that confronts you. This ability to focus your effort so sharply will undoubtedly be of assistance in life.

28–34

You concentrate well but you could do with improvement.

20–27

You concentrate quite well but are distracted too often. You are allowing your mental effort to be frittered away on silly things which don't matter.

under 20

Your concentration is really quite... Erm, would you PAY ATTENTION when I'm speaking to you?

Chinese roulette

I first came across this game of personality revelations in a French film. I remember little of the film itself, but the game stayed with me, and I have tried to reproduce a version of it here. The basic idea is simple. Players take turns to answer a series of questions that may prompt them to make revelations about their personality. It gets even more interesting when the players are called upon to use their intuition to answer the questions about other players in Game 2. I seem to remember that the film version got rather vicious. Naturally my list of questions is by no means exhaustive and, once you have the idea, I'm sure you can make up many more of your own. You need a random method for choosing which player answers which question or, alternatively, for picking a victim about whom the other players must then comment. Names and numbers written on pieces of paper and drawn from a bag will serve the purpose perfectly well. As with all personality assessments, there are no right or wrong answers. The fun is to see how much people reveal about themselves or what they really think about others. They will probably not reveal this intentionally, but by reading between the lines you may be able to work it out. The answers do not need to be concise and you can indulge in as much cross-questioning and analysis as you wish. This game is completely unlike a psychometric questionnaire, which limits your responses to those acceptable to the test designer. Here you can indulge yourself as much as you wish.

Game 1

1 If you were a bird, which bird would you be?

....

2 Which town would you choose to die in?

....

3 If you could be someone famous, who would you be?

....

4 Name the three famous people you admire most.

....

5 If you could choose to know when you will die, would you do so?

....

6 You've been granted three wishes; what are they?

....

7 Which fictional hero do you resemble most?

....

8 Which fictional villain would you like to be?

....

9 Who is your best friend?

....

10 Who do hate most in the whole world?

....

11 What is your greatest virtue?

....

12 What is your worst vice?

....

13 If you had to sing a song about your life, which well-known song would you choose?

....

14 At what age do you think you will die?

....

15 Would you change faces with someone else?

....

16 You have absolute power in your country for one hour; what do you do?

....

17 What job would you do if you could choose anything?

....

18 What is your worst fear?

....

19 Which has been the best day of your life so far?

....

20 Which has been the worst day of your life so far?

....

21 Describe the worst nightmare you have ever had?

....

22 Think of something from your past that embarrasses you even now. What is it?

....

23 Did you love your parents?

....

24 Did your parents love you?

....

25 Are you truly happy with your life?

....

26 Would you marry the same person again?

....

27 Would you sincerely like to be rich?

....

28 You have one month to live; plan the rest of your life.

....

29 What is the worst mistake you ever made?

....

30 Name a brave decision you have never regretted.

....

31 What is the most difficult thing you have ever had to do?

....

Game 2

1 What secret would you most like to know?

....

2 How many members of the opposite sex have you truly loved? (There is obviously a gay version of this question.)

....

3 You are forced to change your name; which name would you choose?

....

4 What would you have written on your gravestone? (You can't opt to be cremated!)

....

5 Choose a fairy story that you think is particularly applicable to you.

....

6 Which fictional character would you like to be?

....

7 Name a job you would love to do if you could choose anything.

....

8 Choose new parents for yourself; give as many details as possible.

....

9 Reinvent your work experience.

....

10 Write your famous last words.

....

11 Assuming you could be a novelist, give the title of your first work.

....

12 Which person from history do you most admire and why?

....

13 Is there a fate worse than death? What is it?

....

14 Your country is engaged in a war that is not its fault, but not yet in any danger of invasion. Would you be prepared to fight?

....

15 Do you believe in life after death?

....

16 Do you believe in heaven and/or hell?

....

17 If you were a car what make would you be?

....

18 If you were a wild animal what would you be?

....

19 Would you really want to meet an alien life form?

....

20 On a scale of 1–10, how generous are you?

....

21 On a scale of 1–10, how honest are you?

....

22 On a scale of 1–10, how good-looking are you?

....

23 Apart from being born, what was the most important event in your life?

....

24 What is your greatest ambition?

....

25 What is your greatest regret?

....

26 If you were to be marooned on a desert island, name one person
– not a member of your family – you would like to be with.

....

27 Name one thing you would like to be remembered for.

....

28 Do you believe that your life has any significance?

....

29 Would you sacrifice your life for anyone else?

....

30 Associate colors with days of the week. Give reasons for your
choices.

....

Game 3

In this game, and the one that follows, a subject is chosen and the
other players are asked questions about him/her.

1 If X was an animal, what animal would s/he be?

....

2 Think of a song that describes X's life.

....

3 Which pop group would X play in if s/he could?

....

4 Which famous person could you envisage X being married to?

....

5 What do you think will be the most significant event of X's life?

....

6 What job, apart from the one s/he actually does, would you think suitable for X?

....

7 Describe X as a character from fiction. The other players must guess who the character is.

....

8 Compose a short eulogy of X.

....

9 What is X's worst fault?

....

10 What is X's most irritating habit?

....

11 Think of X as a plant. What sort of plant would you choose?

....

12 X has to go to a fancy dress party; what costume would be most appropriate?

....

13 If X had a sex change, what new name would you choose?

....

14 What do you most value about X?

....

15 What one thing about X would you most like to change?

....

16 Think of X's life as a book; what title would you choose for him/her?

....

17 Think of X's life as a film. Who would play the part of X? Who do you think X would choose for the part?

....

18 Give X a new name (not a nickname but a real one).

....

19 Give X a new nickname.

....

20 Compose a limerick teasing X in some way.

....

21 Describe X's entry in the school yearbook. (Knowledge of the real entry disqualifies you from attempting this question.)

....

22 Decide what it is about you that most irritates X.

....

23 Imagine X in charge of an expedition in unknown territory; describe how s/he would cope.

....

24 Which famous painter would have chosen X as a model? Give reasons.

....

25 Think of a piece of classical music that reminds you of X. Give reasons.

....

26 Think of a poem that could be about X.

....

27 If people really do have auras, what color will X's be?

....

28 If X were to receive a Nobel prize, what would it be for?

....

29 Some believe there are 'cat people' and 'dog people'. Which is X?

....

Game 4

1 What would you give X as the present of a lifetime?

....

2 Who do you think is X's best friend?

....

3 If X had to emigrate, which country would s/he choose to go to? Why?

....

4 Would X have been a rebel peasant or a courtier?

....

5 Pick a Shakespeare character that X could play convincingly.

....

6 Think of a famous quotation that X might have said.

....

7 Guess X's middle name.

....

8 If X had a motto what would it be?

....

9 Pick a character from an opera who resembles X.

....

10 If you did not know, what nationality would you guess X to be?

....

11 Which character from Greek mythology might X resemble?

....

12 List X's five favorite things.

....

13 List X's best points.

....

14 Recount the funniest thing X has ever said to you.

....

15 On a scale of 1–10, give X marks for sense of humor.

....

16 On a scale of 1–10, give X marks for intuition.

....

17 On a scale of 1–10, give X marks for intelligence.

....

18 Guess which sign of the zodiac X was born under.

....

19 Guess which sign of the Chinese zodiac X was born under.

....

20 Guess who X's favorite author is.

....

21 Guess who X's favorite male and female film stars are.

....

22 What is X's favorite foreign food?

....

23 On a scale of 1–10, how ambitious do you think X is?

....

24 On a scale of 1–10, how attractive do you think X is?

....

25 What job would you give to X?

....

26 What do you think is X's favorite music?

....

27 Given unlimited resources, what sort of house would X live in, and where?

....

28 How would X spend a fortune?

....

29 What do you value most about X?

....

30 What do you think is X's greatest regret?

....

Consequences

This game can be as simple or as complicated as you wish. The basics are quite easy. I give you the beginning of a story and you supply the end. If you play this as a party game, you will probably want to limit your answer to a couple of sentences, but should you wish to spend more time on this exercise you may give your story a more ambitious ending.

1 A group of sailors are shipwrecked on a desert island. Supplies run low and they are forced to resort to cannibalism in order to survive. Eventually they are rescued, but just before their rescuers arrive they manage to hide the evidence of their crimes and swear an oath that they will never tell anyone what happened.

....

....

....

....

2 A young woman works as a hairdresser on low wages. One day a woman customer at the salon where she works tells her that she is beautiful enough to be a model and offers to speak to a contact in the business who might help. To the young woman's amazement she is offered work and is soon very successful. She now earns huge amounts of money but finds that this puts a barrier between her and her family and former friends.

....

....

....

....

3 Three sisters live with their widowed father. The two elder ones marry, move away and lose interest. The youngest daughter gets stuck with looking after her father as he ages. Her chances of an independent life seem to be fading.

....

....

....

....

4 In ancient Greece a man goes to consult the oracle at Delphi. To his surprise the oracle tells him that he will one day be a king. However, in order to achieve this he must leave his family and wander in the wilderness until the time is right for him to meet his fate.

....

....

....

....

....

6

A man is sitting eating with friends in a restaurant. He casually glances out of the window and notices another man approach a young woman who is lounging on the opposite corner of the street. The two talk for a few minutes and then walk off together. The spectator is astonished to realize that the man with the girl is a close family friend whom he has known for many years.

....

....

....

....

7

A woman works for years for the same company and achieves a reasonable degree of success though, as the company is still rather male-dominated, she never seriously considers reaching the top. To everyone's amazement there is a shake-up at boardroom level and she is the only candidate who can get enough votes to be the new chairman. The 'old guard' are clearly outraged by this turn of events.

....

....

....

....

8

A group of friends who are just about to graduate from university gather to make each other a solemn promise. They swear that throughout their lives they will do everything to help each other in every way. They reason that by making such a team effort they will stand a far higher chance of success than they would alone.

....

....

....

....

9

Two men love the same girl. Their passion leads to jealousy, and eventually there is a fight in which, by an appalling accident, the girl is killed. One of the men is blamed for the killing and jailed. Many years later, after his release, the two unexpectedly come face to face again.

....

....

....

Every week, year in year out, a man buys a lottery ticket. He always chooses the same combination of numbers, and although he never wins he enjoys the excitement of looking up the results at the end of the week. One week he finds that he has the winning numbers. However, he cannot find his ticket in the usual pocket of his coat.

....
....
....
....

A man returns from his travels abroad after 10 years. He finds that his family has heard and believed a rumor that he died at sea. His wife has remarried and his children now regard a stranger as their father.

....
....
....
....
....

Analysis

Clearly your personality will have the strongest possible bearing on the way you complete each story. However, since each of us is inevitably trapped inside our own personality, it is hard to appreciate that there can be any other way of thinking and feeling. The most interesting way of playing this game is to compare your stories with those of your friends. It is then that you will start to appreciate just what differences there are between people. Whereas you may always see things from an optimistic viewpoint, you may well find that others view life in a more jaundiced fashion. People very easily slip into the idea that there are 'right' and 'wrong' personalities, and an exercise such as this may help to reveal some of these deep divisions. Do you feel that your friends have simply come up with different endings to the stories, or are you concerned that they have thought of solutions you find unacceptable? To what extent are you prepared to compromise over the endings you have chosen? Just how strongly do you feel about your creative efforts? And speaking of creativity, how easy or difficult did you find it to end the stories at all? For some people the simple ideas presented above will be enough to set off a great chain of thought while others will sit and struggle to find the next sentence.

Heroes and villains

We pick our heroes for the qualities we would like to possess or suspect that we do in fact possess. We pick our villains because they exhibit qualities we particularly despise, though frequently we also find these qualities, deeply buried and hotly denied, in ourselves. Thus our choice of heroes and villains can give significant clues to our personality. Try this game to see what you can discover from your choices. Below you will find groups of well-known heroes and villains. I have included lists for both sexes so that you can also choose qualities you admire in members of the opposite sex. Choose 10 heroes and 10 heroines, as far as possible in order of preference. Write them down in a list. Then choose 10 male and female villains and write these down. You will see that I make no distinction between heroes and villains in the listing. People's ideas on that subject will differ, and it is for you to make the decision. To take an example, until a few years ago many white South Africans would have included Nelson Mandela on their list of villains. Nowadays he would probably be included as a hero by many people. You can make things more interesting by getting your friends to join in. Once each player has compiled his or her own lists, how about trying to assess which heroes, heroines and villains your friends might choose? Comparing lists at the end of the game should provide you with some interesting discussion points.

Bruce Willis	Winston Churchill	Martin Luther King
Nelson Mandela	Winona Ryder	Rudolf Nureyev
'Che' Guevara	Michael Schumacher	Frank Sinatra
Saddam Hussein	Barbra Streisand	Bill Gates
Norman Schwarzkopf	Pope Benedict XVI	Donald Trump
Imelda Marcos	Linda Lovelace	Queen Elizabeth II
Adolf Hitler	Ronald Reagan	Pablo Picasso
Lorena Bobbitt	Pol Pot	Mae West
Rasputin	Marilyn Monroe	Charles Manson
Mikhail Gorbachev	Ayatollah Khomeini	Germaine Greer
Marie Curie	Napoleon Bonaparte	Monica Lewinsky
Prince Charles	Alexander the Great	Jimi Hendrix
Joseph Stalin	Benazir Bhutto	Joan of Arc
Yasser Arafat	Dwight Eisenhower	Madonna
Albert Einstein	Indira Ghandi	Princess Diana
Magic Johnson	Mao Tse Tung (Zedong)	Mother Teresa
Mahatma Gandhi	Sharon Stone	Neil Armstrong
Geri 'Ginger' Halliwell	Sandy Shaw	Margaret Thatcher
Dorothy Parker	Queen Elizabeth I	Eleanor Roosevelt
Clint Eastwood	Jean-Paul Sartre	Hillary Clinton

Pope Benedict XVI	Sharon Stone	Charles Manson
Linda Lovelace	Sandy Shaw	Germaine Greer
Ronald Reagan	Queen Elizabeth I	Monica Lewinsky
Pol Pot	Jean-Paul Sartre	Jimi Hendrix
Marilyn Monroe	Martin Luther King	Joan of Arc
Ayatollah Khomeini	Rudolf Nureyev	Madonna
Napoleon Bonaparte	Frank Sinatra	Princess Diana
Alexander the Great	Bill Gates	Mother Teresa
Benazir Bhutto	Donald Trump	Neil Armstrong
Dwight Eisenhower	Queen Elizabeth II	Margaret Thatcher
Indira Ghandi	Pablo Picasso	Eleanor Roosevelt
Mao Tse Tung (Zedong)	Mae West	Hillary Clinton

heroes	heroines	male and female villains
1.............................	1.............................	1.............................
2.............................	2.............................	2.............................
3.............................	3.............................	3.............................
4.............................	4.............................	4.............................
5.............................	5.............................	5.............................
6.............................	6.............................	6.............................
7.............................	7.............................	7.............................
8.............................	8.............................	8.............................
9.	9.............................	9.............................
10.............................	10.............................	10.............................

Perfection

This game can be played alone or with friends. It consists simply of choosing a 'perfect' life for yourself. Below, you will find a number of categories. In each one, you will be invited to consider what, for you, would constitute perfection. For this purpose you may assume that none of the normal constraints apply. For example, you may choose as your perfect career to be a surgeon even though you do not have the training, or you may choose the life of a small theater actor even though you are aware that you could not manage on the money. At first sight this is little more than daydreaming – and you can certainly play the game that way if you want. If that is what you choose to do, it will already have told you something about your personality. If you want to look deeper into the issues here, then you will quickly discover that you are being asked to assess the life you already lead and decide whether it is what you really want. You will also have the chance to question what sort of person you are and what sort of things bring you happiness. Try to do more than just produce a list of choices. For example, if you decide your perfect partner would be, say, Jodie Foster, try to analyze why you made that choice and what it implies about your personality (and hers). We've given you some room to jot notes if you want to.

1

As a perfect partner I would choose:..

Because: ....

....

....

....

2

My perfect career would be:...

Because: ....

....

....

....

3

My perfect house would be:...

Because: ....

....

....

....

4

My perfect pet would be:..

Because: ....

....

....

....

5

My perfect holiday would be:...

Because: ....

....

....

....

My perfect night out would be:...

Because:...

6
....

....

....

My perfect country of residence would be:...

Because:...

7
....

....

....

My perfect boss would be:...

Because:...

8
....

....

....

My perfect birthday party would be:...

Because:...

9
....

....

....

My perfect meal would be:...

Because:...

10
....

....

....

11

If I could stay at one perfect age it would be: ....

Because: ....

....

....

....

12

My perfect period of history would be: ....

Because: ....

....

....

....

13

My perfect friends would be: ....

Because: ....

....

....

....

14

If I started my own perfect business it would be: ....

Because: ....

....

....

....

15

The thing I'd most like to achieve in my life would be: ....

Because: ....

....

....

....

16

The greatest adventure I could undertake would be:

Because: ....

....

....

....

17

The greatest act of philanthropy I could undertake would be: ....

Because: ....

....

....

....

18

The perfect future I see for my children would be:...

Because: ....

....

....

....

19

The thing that would make me proudest in life would be: ....

Because: ....

....

....

....

20

If I could have written one of the great books it would be:...............................

Because:

....

....

....

21

If I could be a great leader I would be:

Because: ....

....

....

....

Test Forty Nine

Hell

This game is the opposite of Perfection (see page 376). Here you are
asked to consider those things that you really hate in life. Once again,
all the usual constraints can be thrown to the wind. If you hate your
boss, you can say so. If you wish you were married to anyone but the
person you are married to, then this is your chance to come to terms
with that idea. As with Perfection you can play the game alone or in
company, though – as I said before – if you play it with your family
and friends a little discretion may be needed. The idea of the game is
to give you a chance to analyze your feelings about some pretty deep
issues in your life. You can just play it as a light-hearted party game,
but if you want to throw any real light on your personality you need
to give your choices some thought and make a few notes about your
reasoning. We've left some space for you to do this.

1 The thing I dislike most about my partner is:..
Because: ....
....
....
....

2 The last person in the world I would marry is: ....
Because: ....
....
....
....

3 The one job I really could not do would be:..
Because: ....
....
....
....

4 The thing I hate most about my job is:..
Because: ....
....
....
....

5 The country I would least like to live in is: ....
Because: ....
....
....
....

6 The habit I find most disgusting is: ....
Because: ....
....
....
....

7 Something I could never eat is:..
Because: ....
....
....
....

8

The person I hate and despise most in the whole world is: ....

Because: ....

....

....

....

9

My greatest fear is: ....

Because: ....

....

....

....

10

The behavior that arouses the greatest contempt in me is: ....

Because: ....

....

....

....

11

The person I would trust least in the world is: ....

Because: ....

....

....

....

12

The political philosophy that arouses most antipathy in me is: ....

Because: ....

....

....

....

13

The sport I would least like to play is: ....

Because: ....

....

....

....

14

The book I have disliked most is: ....

Because: ....

....

....

....

15

The nation with which I feel least sympathy is: ....

Because: ....

....

....

....

16

The thing that would make me the most angry is:...

Because: ....

....

....

....

17

Of all types of jealousy the one I am most prone to is:: ....

Because: ....

....

....

....

18

The thing I like least about myself is: ....

Because: ....

....

....

....

19

What annoys me most about other people is: ....

Because: ....

....

....

....

20

My greatest failure has been: ....

Because: ....

....

....

21

I think Hell might be like:...

Because: ....

....

....

....

22

To me suicide is:..

Because: ....

....

....

....

23

The type of death that scares me the most is: ....

Because: ....

....

....

....

24

What annoys me most about other people is:...

Because: ....

....

....

....

25

My greatest failure has been: ....

Because: ....

....

....

....

Statistics

Conducting a psychometric test is of little benefit unless its results can be interpreted accurately and used to measure a person's individual abilities against the population as a whole, or at least the particular group of interest. Where the sample (the group of people participating in a test) increases in size, and different tests of varying levels of complexity are introduced, the raw results are rarely very informative. For instance, in terms of relative performance, the 70% raw score a 16-year-old achieves in his or her math assessment cannot be compared to the 54% obtained by a graduate taking a professional accountancy examination. Which of the two performed better cannot be concluded just from this limited information. The performance of the base population, i.e. all 16-year-olds submitting this type of assessment, is consequently used to create a model against which individual scores can be placed to compare their achievements. This statistical model often relies upon what is called the 'Normal distribution,' which the 16-year-old's math assessment will help explain.

Let's assume the math assessment results varied from 40% to 95% and can be represented graphically as shown below:

Out of the 90 pupils, 32 scored 75% or above. This shows that a score of 75% places a candidate at the lower end of the top 35% of pupils, or conversely at the top of the bottom 65%, in the 65th percentile. Clearly the assessment results vary in line with the number of students and the assessment itself. So conclusions comparing the relative performance of a student with another become rather cumbersome when changes in the sample occur, with performances between different assessment groups being largely incomparable. This is where the Normal distribution offers some assistance.

If the assessment results are re-examined, we can see then that the average score is approximately 68%, found by summing all the scores and

dividing by the number of pupils, 90. If the test results are redrawn around this mean, a curve can be fitted to represent an approximate scoring pattern:

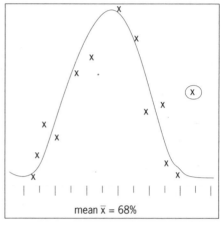

mean x̄ = 68%

This curve is known as the Normal distribution curve. It represents graphically a balanced grouping of scores around the mean, and it is found time and again. The bell-shaped curve shows how, as the score increases or decreases from the mean, so too does the proportion of people achieving each score. As the size of such a sample grows, the pattern of results will always fit the Normal curve more and more closely. This is because if the population as a whole conforms to the Normal pattern, then, as the sample size increases, it becomes better aligned to its parent population, and consequently provides a more accurate basis for comparison. With smaller samples, deviations from the Normal pattern are more likely to occur, i.e., an instance where 8 pupils miraculously score 95% in the assessment. Despite being positioned further away from the Normal curve, the distribution still holds, but its validity may be restricted. This will be explored in more depth later on.

So, as a basis for a model, the Normal distribution can often be applied to events as diverse as psychometric testing and assessing the Australians' affinity for Earl Grey tea. However, certain characteristics intrinsic to the Normal curve render it a unique and an invaluable statistical tool. It always remains symmetrical about the mean, which is represented usually as the peak of the curve. This curve is approximately bell-

shaped, and the area under it is equal to 100%, or 1. This 1 represents the whole population – if the peak point shows the average result, the scores up to that point are achieved by 50% of the pupils. Since the curve is symmetrical, 100% of the scores fall below the entire curve so all performances are accounted for. So just how does the Normal distribution provide a basis for comparison? A process of standardization is required to make results from a multitude of tests comparable.

This involves comparing the actual result with the average score in the context of a test situation, and incorporating a measure of spread, known as the Standard Deviation (SD). This provides a means of measuring numerically the extent to which scores deviate from the mean result. The two following samples emphasize the importance of this. The size of each sample is identical; it is the spread of results that varies. The results of two psychometric tests have been plotted on the two graphs below, each following a Normal distribution. The 'Easy' sample is far more widely spread out about the mean than that of 'Peasy,' which is more closely bunched. The mean = 50, and being the same for both groups, gives no indication of this spread. Enter the standard deviation.

Due to the greater range of results in the 'Easy' test, a score of 40 is far more acceptable than the same grade in 'Peasy,' as here far fewer people scored as low a grade. By applying standard deviations, it is possible to see the relative performance of each 40-scoring candidate. To activate their use, standard deviations are applied to the standardized scores, which enable the mean to be set equal to zero. This is important, as the multitude of means obtained from many different test samples can all be equated to 0 so a basis for comparison is established. The vast majority of a sample's results lie within three standard deviations of the mean. When this mean is equated to 0, this is depicted as shown below:

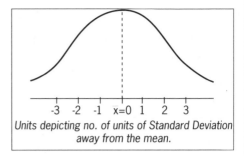

Units depicting no. of units of Standard Deviation away from the mean.

So at point 1, we are one standard deviation above the mean, and at –3, three standard deviations below.

As a rough guide:
68.3% of the population lie within 1 SD about the mean;
95.4% of the population lie within 2 SD about the mean;
99.7% of the population lie within 3 SD about the mean.

So the 'Easy' test would be expected to have a higher standard deviation value than 'Peasy' due to the greater range of results. Simplifying the results in graph form helps to clarify:

Test: no. of candidates obtaining score

Score(%)	Easy	Peasy
10	1	0
20	2	0
30	4	2
40	8	8
50	16	26
60	8	8
70	4	2
80	2	0
90	1	0

The Standard Deviation is found using the expression $SD = \sqrt{\sum a^2 - a^2 n}$
where a = each score, a = mean score, n = sample size, $\sum$ = total sum

In other words, the standard deviation is found by summing the squared values of each score, subtracting the sample size multiplied by the mean value squared, dividing the answer by the sample size minus 1, and square-rooting the result. Applying this to the two samples yields below:

From this then we can see that a score of 66% (50+16.1%) from the 'Easy' test is roughly equivalent to one of 58% (50+8.4%) for 'Peasy,' both scores being 1 standard deviation above the mean. This method of judging a performance by the number of standard deviations that separate it from the mean can be helpful.

Easy
$\sum a^2 = 1(10^2) + 2(20^2) + 4(30^2) + 8(40^2) + 16(50^2) + 8(60^2) + 4(70^2) + 2(80^2) + 1(90^2)$
    $= 126{,}600$
$x = [1(10) + 2(20) + 4(30) + 8(40) + 16(50) + 8(60) + 4(70) + 2(80) + 1(90)] \div 46$
    $= 50$
$x^2 = 50^2 = 2500$
$n - 1 = 45$
$= \quad SD = \sqrt{\dfrac{126{,}600 - (46 \times 2500)}{45}} = 16.1$ *(to 1 decimal place)*

peasy
$\sum a^2 \quad = 2(30^2) + 8(40^2) + 26(50^2) + 8(60^2) + 2(70^2) = 118{,}200$
$x \quad = [2(30) + 8(40) + 26(50) + 8(60) + 2(70)] \div 46 = 50$
$x^2 \quad = 50^2 = 2500$
$n - 1 = 45$
$= SD = \sqrt{\dfrac{118{,}200 - (46 \times 2500)}{45}} = 8.4$ *(to 1 decimal place)*

To find a standardized score, **z**, of a particular raw score, the mean is subtracted from the raw score, and this is then divided by the standard deviation. So for the two scores of 40%:

$$Z \text{ easy} = \frac{40 - 50}{16.1} = -0.6$$

$$Z \text{ peasy} = \frac{40 - 50}{8.4} = -1.2$$

Each score of 40 can thus be compared on the following standardized Normal curves:

Use of statistical tables shows that 0.27, or 27% of the population, would be expected to achieve a mark of 40% or below in the 'Easy' test and 0.12, or 12% in 'Peasy'.

Thus since –0.6 is larger than –1.2, the scorer of 40 in 'Easy' has achieved a better result than that of 'Peasy'. Since test results are extremely unlikely to fall beyond three standard deviations either side of the mean, the chances of scoring below 25% and above 75% for the 'Peasy' test are virtually non-existent. This is less illuminating with the 'Easy' test: we conclude that results are likely to fall in the region 2%–98%, indicative of its far greater spread of results.

Importantly, the application of the Normal distribution is not restricted to groups of the same sample size. The 'Easy/Peasy' examples take advantage of this fact to simplify the explanatory analysis. Rather, the Normal's merit lies in the fact that the test and standard deviation process can be applied to any set of test scores, regardless of test type, the scoring process and units used, and the mean and range of results.

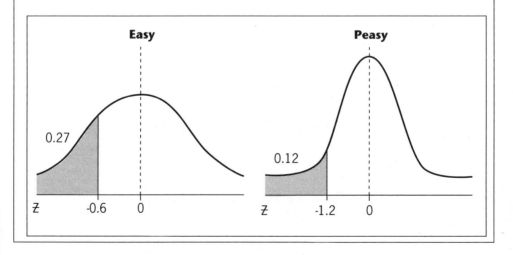

Consequently, standard deviations are incorporated into the psychometric test-scoring process to help predict the proportion of people likely to achieve a test score lying between a specified number of standard deviations. For a psychometric test to be effective, it is essential to know the mean and standard deviation of the parent population either from existing data or from calculations using as large a relevant sample as possible. Using a relevant parent population or sample for this is absolutely vital in order for results to be accurately interpreted: standardizing the 16-year-olds' maths assessment mark by using the average mean mark for the same assessment obtained by a group of graduate statisticians is blatantly nonsensical. Due to this, for a particular test, various Normal tables may exist for different groups of people to allow reasonable comparisons to be made.

The use of the Normal distribution tables to assess psychometric test results is sometimes rejected in favor of converting the raw standardized z values to a scoring scale, the most popular of these being the stanine, sten and T-score scales. The same standardizing process is implemented; z scores are simply manipulated to form different bases for comparison.

All three scales are established by multiplying the **z** score by a certain factor, and adding this to their own particular mean. The sten and stanine scales both split their ranges up between two standard deviations about the mean, the former method being favoured by personality test assessment. In contrast, the T-score can span beyond three standard deviations. Computation is as follows:

Stanine x= 2 Z+5 1<x<10 x=5

Sten x= 2 Z+5.5 1<x<9   x=5.5

T-score x= 10Z+50 30<x<80 x=50

Reliability and validity

Regardless of the length and complexity of a test, if it flounders in the reliability and validity stakes, it is of little use. A test has to be assessed in terms of both of these factors in order to ascertain how much it can be relied upon.

Should the same person take the same test on two consecutive occasions, the results should be very similar. The extent to which this consistency occurs is considered to be the reliability level of a test, or the margin of error. By comparison, rather than questioning test accuracy, validity considers whether a test assesses what it claims to, e.g., does a numeracy test actually gauge numeracy or just learning skills? The four main types of reliability and validity that are of interest in the psychometric testing are:

Test-retest
Determines a test's overall consistency

Construct
Measures how well a test assesses what it claims to

Internal consistency
Judges to what extent random groups of questions within a test assess the same thing

Criterion-related
Questions if a test can be practicably applied with objective, tangible results of some specified criterion, or if this criterion is too abstract and immeasurable

Clearly the nature of a psychometric test determines which strands of reliability and validity are of most concern. Since this varies with each situation (e.g., different tests may aim to have high internal consistency rather than high criterion-related validity), combining a number of these contrasting tests helps to ensure that a balance of objectives is achieved.

Aside from the subjective appraisal of a test's reliability and validity, another statistical tool is on hand to quantify a test's performance in this domain: the correlation coefficient, **r**. This is used to measure the reliability and validity of tests by calculating the degree of association between two variables. A high correlation coefficient is obtained when both variables, or items of interest, are strongly related to each other (see Figure **a** below). When one thing has little impact on the other's value, the correlation coefficient will be low (see Figure **b** on p.29). The following scattergrams exemplify both situations where each cross corresponds to an instance in which corresponding values on the horizontal and vertical axis simultaneously occur.

Figure **a** demonstrates that the older the student, the higher the grade obtained in the standard maths assessment, as a rule. We can conclude that the correlation coefficient will be high. In contrast, the very low correlation between daily tea consumption and assessment performance shows how one cannot predict the other; the two are unrelated. As the dots veer further away from the line representing the linear relationship between variables, as in (a), the relationship becomes weaker and harder to define. Consequently, the value of the correlation coefficient falls towards 0. The correlation can vary in value from -1 to 1:

r = 1

The closer the correlation coefficient to 1, the more perfect and definable the relationship.

r = 0

The closer the correlation coefficient to 0, the more negligible and less definable the relationship.

r = –1

The closer the correlation coefficient to –1, the more perfect but negative the rela-tionship: as one variable falls, the other rises.

Demand for computers (y-axis)
Price of computers (x-axis)
eg r=-0.92

(a)
Moderate test – retest reliability r=0.49
Easy test score, 1 week later (y-axis)
Easy test score, 1st attempt (x-axis)

The correlation coefficient will rarely identify a perfect relationship because numerous other factors are often involved: the higher the price of computers, the lower the demand, but demand may also be affected by advertising, availability, computer performance and the state of the economy. So when using the correlation coefficient to assess the reliability and validity of psychometric tests, it is essential to consider the other factors involved.

(b)
High internal consistency reliablity r=0.89
Results of even numbered Peasy test questions (y-axis)
Results of odd numbered Peasy test questions (x-axis)

The correlation coefficient is used to aid the analysis, not to act as its sole determinant.

In a specific psychometric test situation, the correlation coefficient is used as a guide, and can be applied to the four key reliability and validity concerns already mentioned:

Validity is of particular interest when considering the likelihood of making incorrect judgements from test results. In the case of (c), a test may prove to be invalid when a low score in the management skills test later proves to be a poor indication of the actual high practical management performance. The importance of these validity

(c)
Low constrict validity
r=0.11

Practically assesed management performance

Management skills test results

(d)
High interior-related validity
r=0.91

No. of mistakes made at work

Attention to detail test result

tests is, then, in determining what proportion of test results will reflect accurately a candidate's true abilities and potential. Finding the ratio of likely correct-to-incorrect decisions helps determine this. Consequently, psychometric tests are rarely the sole means of selection, but are used in conjunction with a more personal, subjective approach.

Being harder to determine than reliability, acceptable levels of validity vary in accordance with both the test and previous selection procedures. Despite some low levels of test validity, the recent rise in popularity of psychometric testing

in the selection process stems from the frequently lower validity of alternative assessment methods on offer. Given that psychometric tests are predominantly used in an interview/selection process, their results can be far more illuminating than any 20-minute interrogation. Should the validity of a test be low, the interviewer should realize this and gear his or her questions to reveal the true validity of an individual's test result. If you already know and understand what your psychometric test is likely to indicate, you are better equipped to argue against any misleading shortcomings it may expose.

Glossary

Abnormal

Broadly speaking, abnormal behavior is not just "different" – if should affect both the sufferer and others in the following ways:

- it is rare, unusual or infrequent (that is, not necessarily characteristic of the person as he or she usually behaves or feels);
- it appears to be rooted in faulty perception or interpretation of reality;
- it is socially unacceptable in ways that go beyond simply "rude" or "inconsiderate";
- it causes distress both to the person and others;
- it is either self-defeating or dangerous.

Agoraphobia

An irrational fear of open or crowded spaces, which leads a person to withdrawing from society and (usually) remaining isolated at home.

Aggression

The use of force, usually inappropriately. Verbal or physical aggression is thought to be a way to cope with threat; invariably, however, it heightens conflict because it provokes the need for retaliation.

Ambivalence

Being of two minds or having conflicting feelings about a person or thing; many therapists stress the need to "contain" conflicting feelings.

Antisocial

Describes someone who is in frequent conflict with society, who is not deterred from conflict by threats of punishment, and who experiences little or no guilt about such conflict.

Anxiety

A state characterized by feelings of fear, dread and foreboding. So-called anxiety disorders are usually accompanied by rapid heartbeat, tension or shakiness. *See also* Panic Attack and Phobia.

Amnesia

Loss of memory, which may be the result of a traumatic event, or physical, psychological or physiological causes.

Behavior therapy

An approach that seeks to change unproductive or self-limiting behavior rather than examine root causes or childhood patterns as a possible source of such behavior.

Bipolar disorder

Another name for manic-depression in which there are mood swings from elation to depression.

Claustrophobia

A fear of small or enclosed spaces, which usually arouses acute anxiety.

Coping

Describes beliefs and behavior that helps us to deal effectively with situations. Defensive coping may allow us time to marshal our resources but not always deal with the source of stress; it includes withdrawal, inappropriate fantasizing, aggressive behavior, and alcohol abuse. Active coping begins with accepting responsibility for our behavior, thoughts and emotions, and tries to deal directly with the cause of stress.

Cognition

The mental process that describes how we learn and how our perceptions and judgments are formed.

Cognitive therapy

An approach that attempts to help people change by examining what they think or believe (their attitudes and expectations). Most commonly, it is used to change negative, self-defeating or self-destructive thoughts into positive ones.

Compulsion

An almost irresistible urge to feel or act in a way that disrupts daily life; people who are compulsive are compelled to perform actions against their conscious choice (constant hand-washing is a type of compulsive behavior). The behavior is an attempt to relieve an underlying anxiety.

Conditioning

A simple form of learning in which associations are formed between certain stimuli and responses.

Consciousness

Awareness. This can be sensory awareness of the environment, or direct inner awareness (knowledge of your own thoughts, feelings, and memories, which do not always rely on sensory organs). "Altered states of consciousness" occur as a result of sleep, dreams, meditation, and hypnotic "trances".

Defense

A way we learn to protect ourselves. Knowledge is a way to avoid pain and danger, so we need to know, for example, that fire is hot and might burn us. However, people who have too many "defense mechanisms" are probably overly or inappropriately suspicious of others. If a child is rejected by a parent, he or she might become deliberately aloof from others; this might control feelings of anguish or pain but also make intimacy with others very difficult.

Delusion

A false or exaggerated belief.

Denial

A defense mechanism in which people believe that threatening or dangerous events or situations are harmless to themselves or others. Denial is an attempt to ward off stress, but should be superseded by genuine and effective ways to deal with difficulties. Smokers often deny the link to cancer, or accept the risk but believe that they are in no danger.

Depressant

Anything that slows down activities or responses. Used excessively, alcohol is a well-known depressant insofar as it is believed to be a way to reduce tension and anxiety.

Depression

Profound feelings of anguish, self-doubt, sadness, and hopelessness. Many believe that depression is an illness, and treatment includes carefully prescribed drugs. Another theory suggests that "learned helplessness" is a possible cause of withdrawn and ineffectual behavior.

Developmental psychology

A field of study that looks at the changes – physical, emotional, cognitive, and social – that occur throughout our life span, and the things that cause such changes (including genetic and environmental factors).

Displacement

Feelings that are deliberately shifted (either consciously or unconsciously) from their original or intended object and directed elsewhere. The substitute or symbols then become the focus of feelings. For example, people often mistreat family members because they are reluctant or unable to express anger toward authority figures.

Ego
The part of ourselves we usually associate with a conscious, everyday identity and "reality."

Empathy
The capacity to imagine the feelings of other people without losing one's own identity.

Envy
Resentment of something that someone else has, rooted in the desire to have it oneself. If not checked, envy will lead to the destruction of whatever the other person has.

Fixation
Describes the experience of being "stuck" at a particular point of development. For example, young adults who are fearful of their ability to cope with responsibilities at work may act like adolescents and be unpunctual or extremely disorganized.

Group therapy
A type of therapy that relies on the insights and support of group members rather than one trained counselor. The shared experience of group members can be an effective spur to changing behavior.

Guilt
A sense of wrong-doing that arises from the real or imagined transgressing of moral, religious or social standards.

Hallucination
A psychiatric term used to describe a sensory experience (that is, seeing, hearing, or otherwise perceiving something) outside of oneself that is not present or does not exist in reality.

Hypnotherapy
The use of a trance-like state to restructure compulsive behavior (such as smoking) or to uncover long-buried feelings and memories. It appears to work by making the subject more relaxed, by narrowing the focus of attention, and by heightening suggestibility.

Hypochondria
The persistent belief that one is suffering from a serious disease although no medical evidence can be found; charactized by undue preoccupation with minor physical sensations and unreasonable fear.

Illusion
The misinterpretation of a real experience (unlike a hallucination, which is the creation of something unreal, and a delusion, which is a false belief).

Introspection
Looking inward in an attempt to describe one's beliefs and feelings objectively.

Jealousy
Feelings of hostility or hurt due to the exclusivity of a relationship between other people.

Libido
According to Freud, the psychological energy that describes the will to live, and is most obvious in the sexual drive.

Locus of control
The place where we attribute control over the receiving of "reinforcers." People with an internal locus of control tend to be highly motivated, have high self-esteem, and believe they can modify the impact of negative events – in short, that they are the source of value and direction in their lives.

Mania
Describes feelings and behavior of uncontrollable elation, often accompanied by sleeplessness and reckless hyperactivity.

Narcissism
Feelings of self-love, which can be a source of self-esteem, or (if distorted) exaggerated self-importance and manipulative behavior.

Neurosis
A psychological disturbance, usually due to inner conflict, accompanied by fears or obsessions that are due to a "partial view" of the person's situation.

Obsession
A persistent, disturbing preoccupation rooted in an unreasonable or distorted perception.

Panic attack
An episode of extreme fear, often accompanied by the fear of "going crazy" or losing control, heavy sweating, trembling, difficulty in breathing, and pounding of the heart; often there is no clear connection between external events and the attack.

Paranoia
A disorder characterized by extreme and persistent delusions that one is being persecuted, talked about, or is the focus of other people's destructive impulses.

Phobia
An unreasonable or exaggerated fear in the presence of a particular object (such as spiders) or situations.

Projection
A psychological defense in which you attibute to other people the feelings or quality that you deplore or wish to disown in yourself.

Psychoanalysis
A system developed by Sigmund Freud for analyzing feelings. He believed that one could uncover the roots of behavior in unconscious motivations and conflicts.

Repression
A defense in which people are not conscious of the negative feelings and events that are locked away in memory because they are unacceptable or too frightening to the conscious mind.

Superego
According to Freudian theory, the part of the personality that has taken on outside social values and is therefore involved in judgement, self-observation, and (often) criticism.

Suppression,
Unlike repression, this is a conscious and deliberate turning away from unacceptable thoughts, feelings, or impulses.